MAYD

On April 26th 1986 at 1.23 a.m., nuclear reactor Unit No. 4 of the Chernobyl nuclear power plant went out of control, triggering the worst nuclear accident in history. A few tired technicians and engineers, struggling to complete a routine experiment on the reactor, had touched off a disaster that killed thirty-one people, forced more than 135,000 people to flee their homes, put tens of thousands under the threat of radiation-induced cancers and polluted an area of the Soviet Union as large as Luxembourg. The drifting winds spread the fallout across Europe even as politicians and nuclear power supporters insisted that there was no real danger.

'Very well constructed, highly accurate and presents a dramatic and excellently written story of what really happened at Chernobyl . . . Chernobyl was not only a tragedy but could be a wakening experience for the Soviet public. This book is a contribution to this process . . .'

Dr Zhores Medvedev, author of *The Rise and Fall of T. D. Lysenko*, *Ten Years after Ivan Denisovich*, *Gorbachev* and, with Roy Medvedev, *A Question of Madness* and *Khrushchev: The Years in Power*.

About the authors

Stuart Parrott and Henry Hamman are both jour-
nalists employed by Radio Free Europe/Radio
Liberty. They are based in London where Ham-
man is bureau chief and Parrott is correspondent.
They are in a unique position to report on events in
East Europe and the Soviet Union.

Parrott is an expert on Eastern European politics
and has also written extensively on Soviet environmental policies and peace movements, east and
west. Hamman covers Soviet energy developments and defence and foreign policy issues. He
wrote extensively about nuclear power and other
environmental controversies in the United States.
He has also written a novel, LAPIS, a thriller set in
Afghanistan.

MAYDAY AT CHERNOBYL

Henry Hamman and Stuart Parrott

NEW ENGLISH LIBRARY

For Our Families

Copyright © 1987 by Henry Hamman
and Stuart Parrott

First published in Great Britain in 1987
by New English Library paperbacks

British Library C.I.P.

Hamman, Henry
    Mayday at Chernobyl.
    1. Nuclear power plants – Ukraine –
    Chernobyl – Accidents.
    I. Title   II. Parrott, Stuart
    363.1'79   TK1362.S65C4

ISBN 0-450-40858-2

Printed and bound in Great Britain for
Hodder and Stoughton Paperbacks, a
division of Hodder and Stoughton Ltd.,
Mill Road, Dunton Green, Sevenoaks,
Kent (Editorial Office: 47 Bedford
Square, London WC1B 3DP) by
Richard Clay Ltd., Bungay, Suffolk.
Photoset by Rowland Phototypesetting Ltd.,
Bury St Edmunds, Suffolk.

CONTENTS

ACKNOWLEDGMENTS

Though two names are listed as the authors, this book could not have been written without the help of many others. Telling the story of Chernobyl requires so much specialised knowledge – of physics, engineering, biology, Soviet affairs, history, to name a few areas – that it is obviously impossible for journalists like ourselves to cope without tremendous assistance. Fortunately for us, that assistance has been generously given.

Among those who helped, we must first thank Dana Powers of Sandia National Laboratories, Albuquerque, New Mexico, who guided us through the complexities of the actual disaster. We were given assistance on the medical aspects of Chernobyl by Barrie Lambert of St Bartholomew's Hospital, London. Working for Radio Free Europe/Radio Liberty allowed us to draw upon the work and advice of some of the finest analysts of Soviet and East European affairs anywhere. Among those to whom we owe particular thanks are Keith Bush, Toomas Ilves, Allan Kroncher and Vera Tolz. But we also used the work of many others from both radios' research departments. At the International Atomic Energy Agency, we were assisted in covering the Chernobyl story by two of the finest press officers with whom we have ever worked: James Dalleish and Hans Freidrich Meyer.

A number of experts on the Soviet and East European economies gave us their time and advice. Among them were Albina Tretyakova Birman and Matthew Sagers of the US Bureau of the Census, Ed. A. Hewitt of the Brookings Institution, John P. Hardt of the US Congressional

Research Service and Jan Vanous of the Washington consulting firm PlanEcon. In London, Tony Scanlan shared his immense knowledge of the Soviet oil industry. Among our fellow journalists, we must particularly thank Larry Tye of *The Boston Globe* and Robert Gillette, until recently the Warsaw correspondent of *The Los Angeles Times*. Like all journalists, we have freely used the work of these and many other fine reporters. Peter Murphy of UK Trustbuilders contributed much to our understanding of Eastern European and Soviet unofficial anti-nuclear activism.

All these people and many more helped make this book as accurate as it is. Needless to say, the errors of fact and interpretation that remain are our responsibility, not theirs.

The book could not have been written without the support of our employers. From the president of RFE/RL, Gene Pell, on down, we have been given encouragement and support. The director of the Central News Division, Jim Edwards, and the deputy director, Barry Griffiths, have put up with disrupted work schedules and have allowed us to follow the story. Maureen McCabe helped with her efficient research. And in London, Annette McGill kept the bureau functioning during a difficult time. Richard Gollner and Neil Hornick are owed special thanks.

It is customary to thank spouses, but in this case the thanks are more than just pro forma. Andrea Parrott and Kathleen Hamman, more than any other people, are responsible for the fact that this book actually got written: it was probably easier for us to do the writing than for them to put up with us.

Of course, a list like this must be incomplete. Some people talked to us but had to do so privately. And we could not mention every name. But all those who helped know it and to them we say: Thank You.

Henry Hamman and Stuart Parrott
London, February 1987

1

MAY DAY/MAYDAY

May Day was marked by a festive mood in the Ukrainian SSR.

Radio Kiev Domestic Service[1]

On the morning of May 1st, 1986, Soviet Communist Party
General Secretary Mikhail Gorbachev mounted the steps
of Lenin's granite tomb in Red Square. He was followed by
members of the Politburo, the supreme policy-making
authority of the party, and by top-ranking members of the
Soviet military. Despite bright sunshine and temperatures
nudging 20 degrees centigrade, Gorbachev, like President
Andrei Gromyko and Prime Minister Nikolai Ryzhkov,
wore the Kremlin uniform of homburg and overcoat.
Other senior Soviet leaders joined Gorbachev on top of
the mausoleum – Shevardnadze, Chebrikov, Ligachev,
Solomentsev, Vorotnikov, Zaikov, Aliev, and the rest of
the Politburo, men almost unknown to the outside world.
Gorbachev's wife, Raisa, in a black outfit and black hat, his
daughter, Irina, and granddaughter, Oksana, were in a
nearby reviewing stand.[2]

The Soviet leadership had gathered near the fortress
walls of the Kremlin and the onion domes of St Basil's
Cathedral for one of the most important ceremonies in the
Communist calendar – the annual May Day Parade. May
Day is celebrated world-wide as a day of international
labour solidarity. But nowhere is it observed with more
seriousness than in the Soviet Union.

The May Day Parade, like the November anniversary parade marking the 1917 Bolshevik seizure of power, offers the Soviet Communist Party an opportunity to mobilise the Soviet people in a great outdoor celebration of the ideals and victories of Communism. Red Square is turned into an amphitheatre for the march-past of thousands upon thousands of workers, students and gymnasts, in colourful processions orchestrated by festive music and loudspeaker slogans.[3]

The amplified slogans boom out across the vast square: 'Workers of the World Unite', 'Communism will over-come', 'Lenin is our Banner'. The marchers wave red flags and banners, carry bouquets of apple blossoms and helium balloons, or hold aloft idealised portraits of Lenin and the Politburo members. The fact that the Soviet leadership reviews the parade from Lenin's Tomb is part of the ritual. The Soviet Communist Party venerates Lenin, the architect of the seizure of power by the Bolshevik Party in October, 1917; Lenin's Tomb, displaying his embalmed body in a brightly-lit glass coffin, is a national shrine.

The May Day parades are a curiously old-fashioned legacy of the early years of the revolutionary Soviet state. They belong to an age when the Bolsheviks had to inspire the masses with the battle slogans of the new order. What was spontaneous in the early years of the Soviet state has become set in an unbreakable mould, hallowed by tradition.[4] Today, many Soviet citizens are immune to the slogans, and make jokes about the pretensions of Communism. But they turn out on the streets each year because one of the requirements of the Party is that people participate in the rites and rituals of Communism. The American journalist, Hedrick Smith, former Moscow correspondent of *The New York Times*, has observed that, just as the Russian Orthodox Church used to place more emphasis on ceremony than theology, so the Soviet Communist Party today places more stress on ritual than belief.

Gorbachev was reviewing his second May Day Parade

as Soviet leader. He had been chosen as Party General
Secretary in March 1985, after the death of Konstantin
Chernenko. The decision by the Politburo to select their
youngest member (Gorbachev was 54) was widely seen as
an attempt to answer a yearning for change in the Soviet
Union. It was seen as a bid to break with the past, and to
give the Soviet Union a new and dynamic leadership after
the immobility of the Brezhnev years.

Gorbachev was something rare: a Soviet politician with
a charismatic style that was a refreshing contrast with
the anonymity of the Old Guard – Brezhnev, Andropov,
Chernenko, all of them recently laid to rest in the Kremlin
Wall. Gorbachev had been hailed with excitement by the
Western media. The British press called him 'a golden
boy', while *The Sunday Times* said, 'a Red Star has Risen in
the East.'

Yet the stocky man who, in 1985, had become the eighth
leader of the Soviet Union, had an orthodox party background. He had risen through its ranks quickly (he entered
the Politburo as a full member before his fiftieth birthday)
reputedly because his patron was the late Mikhail Suslov,
the guardian of the Soviet Union's ideological grail.
Gorbachev himself had formerly held responsibility for
ideology and party affairs. He was the holder of three
Orders of Lenin. He constantly stressed the legacy of Lenin
to legitimise his programme of reforms. His presence on
Lenin's Tomb reflected continuity.

On May Day, the Soviet Union began a four-day public
holiday that was to end on May 4th, the Russian Orthodox
Easter. Tens of thousands of Soviet workers, students and
children were taking part in the May Day Parade, and
Red Square was packed with spectators. All the municipal
districts of Moscow, and major factories, universities and
research institutes, had contributed contingents of
marchers. Walking along the main roads of Moscow, they
began converging on the centre of the city soon after dawn.
Others travelled to the parade in trolley buses that flew
little red flags in honour of May Day.

Similar parades were held all over the Soviet Union, from its largest cities to its dustiest provincial towns, with staggered timing to reflect the different time zones in a country which occupies one-sixth of the land area of the earth. The May Day celebrations had begun in the Far Eastern provinces of Siberia when it was still midnight in Moscow. Representatives of the more than a hundred nationalities in the Soviet Union – Russians, Ukrainians, Georgians, Byelorussians, Uzbeks, Kazakhs, Lithuanians – joined in the parades. The May Day festivities extended into space where two cosmonauts, Leonid Kizin and Vladimir Solovyov, were manning the *Mir* (Peace) satellite. They beamed a message to earth: 'We are celebrating May Day in space.'

The image presented by Soviet television on May Day was of millions of people across the nation joining together in a spontaneous affirmation of the achievements of socialist labour. The reality was that the celebrations were choreographed (with all the precision, attention to detail and old-fashioned ritual of a Trooping the Colour or Royal Wedding) by party activists whose job is to mobilise public support for such demonstrations of mass participation.

At the stroke of 10 o'clock, when the full Politburo emerged, the loudspeakers around Red Square sounded a fanfare and blared out the first slogan which had been chosen for May Day, 1986: 'Long Live May Day, the day of international solidarity of working people. Proletarians of the world unite.' This was the signal for the parade to begin.

Over the next two hours, the marchers paraded past Lenin's Mausoleum in lines nine-abreast, shoulder to shoulder. The festive parade was orchestrated by the playing of the *Internationale* and other socialist anthems. Carnival floats, illustrating themes of workers' solidarity or international socialist cooperation, punctuated the procession. People carried portraits of Lenin, flags of the nation's fifteen republics and balloons inscribed with 'Peace'. Some

banners had anti-American themes. One slogan proclaimed, 'No to Nuclear Madness.'

Throughout the parade, the loudspeakers relayed the
slogans of May Day, 1986. The list of forty slogans had been
chosen by the Central Committee, the body which directs
party activities. Some slogans were general assertions
about the victory of Communism: 'Long live the unbreakable alliance of the working class, the peasantry and the
intelligentsia,' 'Glory to the valiant armed forces of the
USSR,' 'Glory to the Soviet women – patriots, working
people and mothers.'[5] Other slogans were more specific.
They were addressed to the nation's workforce, urging it to
greater effort, better discipline and higher productivity,
and exhorting it to meet the targets of the twelfth Five-Year
Plan which had been adopted by the twenty-seventh Soviet
Party Congress two months earlier. These slogans emphasised Soviet economic and industrial priorities:

Working people of the Soviet Union. Let us achieve
a decisive breakthrough in the development of the
national economy. Let us ensure a sharp turn
toward an economy of high-level organisation and
efficiency.

Soviet scientists. The country expects from you revolutionary discoveries and inventions in the technical sphere
and technology. Increase the effectiveness of scientific
research work and be more energetic in applying it more
closely to production needs.

Machine builders. You are at the leading edge of
the technical re-tooling of the national economy.
Speed up the creation of highly productive, reliable and
economical machines, equipment and instruments.

In the idealistic fervour of the young Bolshevik state, the
marchers in the Red Square parades used to chant these
battle-cries as they marched past Lenin's Tomb, vying with
each other to see who could shout the loudest. Today, the
slogans are no longer chanted by the marchers.

By midday, the elaborate parade was over. The Moscow metro stations reopened, the road blocks were removed and the Soviet people settled down for their four-day holiday. Western correspondents noted that there were some differences about the May Day celebrations in 1986. The heavy adulation of the leadership traditional in the May Day parades was absent. Gorbachev had discouraged the cult of personality: there were only a few portraits of him on show. The Western correspondents also noted that, unlike previous years, there were no slogans referring to the Soviet nuclear power industry.

*   *   *

While the May Day Parade was being staged in Red Square, Soviet officials at the Ukrainian town of Pripyat, 400 miles to the south west of Moscow, were struggling to cope with the world's worst nuclear accident at the Chernobyl power plant.

MI8 helicopters spent all day flying repeated missions over the power plant on the banks of the Pripyat River. Hour after hour, the routine did not change. The helicopter pilots flew to a spot directly above the caved-in roof of the No. 4 reactor unit. They manoeuvred precisely before dumping their loads into its smoking interior. As one helicopter veered off, another took its place. From a distance, it looked as if the helicopters were dropping bombs on the building. But there were no explosions, no flashes of fire, no noise except the sound of engines throttled to full power.

The helicopter pilots, when they looked down, could see straight into the heart of the reactor. It glowed an incandescent hot orange. It was a bright spring day. For miles around, the farmlands, lakes, forests and marshes of this sleepy agricultural area appeared tranquil. But the landscape below the helicopters was nearly deserted. Fields were empty of livestock. There were no anglers on the banks of the Pripyat River. In the distance, long lines of heavily-loaded trucks were plying back and forth on the Kiev–Chernobyl highway.

Five days earlier, at 1.23 a.m. on Saturday, April 26th, the reactor had exploded when its nuclear reaction suddenly went out of control. Two blasts, seconds apart, blew off the top of the building, set off at least thirty fires, strewed radioactive debris for miles around the plant and shot plumes of radioactive gases and particles more than a kilometre into the night sky. It was the worst accident in the thirty-two-year history of commercial nuclear power. In a few terrifying seconds Chernobyl joined Hiroshima and Nagasaki as a casualty of the nuclear age.

The Soviet military pilots, some of them veterans of the wars in Afghanistan and Ethiopia, flew repeated missions on May Day in an attempt to smother the uranium and graphite core of the reactor. The core, 1,700 tons of graphite holding 218 tons of uranium dioxide, was burning at a temperature of more than 2,000 degrees centigrade. It was still spewing radio-active poisons into the atmosphere. The helicopter pilots dropped bags of lead, sand, clay, dolomite and boron carbide into the reactor core in a desperate attempt to stop the radioactive release and put out the fire inside.

The pilots flew in conditions more hazardous than anything they had encountered in combat. They had to fly directly into the plumes of radioactive gases and particles. Their helicopters had been hurriedly fitted with lead shields, and the crews wore protective clothing. But they could spend only a few seconds over their target. An air traffic controller led them to the target: 'There are one hundred metres, fifty, thirty, ten, five, three, two, one metre before the target, drop the cargo.' The pilots had to manoeuvre past the hazard of the tall chimney of the reactor. Thermal updrafts from the reactor core made the positioning of the helicopters even more difficult. Reconnaissance planes flew over the reactor to take photographs and radiation counts.

The Chernobyl power station, with its four 1,000-megawatt reactor units, lies on the outskirts of Pripyat,

south-east of the Yanov railway station on the high right
bank of the slow-running Pripyat River. It normally generated more than ten per cent of the electricity used by the
forty-five million people of the Ukraine and also supplied
power to Eastern Europe. But, on May Day, it was silent.
Its great turbogenerators were idle, and no electricity
flowed through the high voltage lines running off towards
the Ukrainian capital of Kiev, eighty miles to the south.
Hours after the fourth reactor exploded, workers had
closed down the third working unit, and twenty-four hours
later, they had shut down the other two operating units.

The situation around the power station resembled a
scene from a science fiction film. Troops from chemical
units in protective suits and masks worked to clear chunks
of highly radioactive material from the grounds. Other
soldiers in eerie protective garb hosed down buildings and
trees with water and sprayed a liquid polymer that would
dry to a film and trap radioactive dust. Occasionally, a
lead-shielded truck from the radiation monitoring service
drove past the five-storey reactor building. Masked militiamen were on duty at traffic intersections. Anyone entering
a six-mile exclusion zone around the reactor needed a
special pass to be permitted to drive through the roadblocks
that marked the zone.

Of the hundreds of workers who would normally be on
duty at the station, only a few volunteer plant employees
were at Chernobyl on May Day. The volunteers were
taking it in turns to work in shifts of fifty to sixty people.
The shifts worked around the clock to keep the three
undamaged reactors in a safe shut-down condition and to
take measurements of radioactivity on the site. Like the
helicopter pilots, they were exposing themselves to potentially lethal dosages of radioactivity. Some areas around the
nuclear reactor were so contaminated that workers could
enter them only for a few minutes, or even seconds. They
were timed as they dashed into radiation-soaked areas to
carry out essential jobs. Workers travelled to the site in
armoured personnel carriers.

At the village of Chistogalovka, three miles south of the power plant, a group of local truck drivers had, for the past three days, been digging clay to be dumped on the reactor core. They worked in conditions of high background radiation. On May Day some of the drivers began to suffer the first symptoms of radiation sickness: nausea, vomiting, diarrhoea, fever. Truck driver S. Fomin was quoted by *Pravda* as saying he had to take charge of the operation because of the 'inaction' of his boss, the chief of the transportation unit at the Chernobyl plant. Fomin told *Pravda*: 'I wouldn't want readers to form a bad impression of our collective because of a few cowards.' Some of the truck drivers were sent to hospital with symptoms of radiation sickness on May 2nd.[6]

The Chernobyl station lay just outside the new town of Pripyat, which was built in the 1970s to accommodate the power station workers and their families. A sleepy provincial place, it was typical of the workers' settlements (*rabochy posyolki*) which are widespread in the Soviet Union. It comprised dozens of white prefabricated high-rise apartment buildings set in square monotonous blocks adjoining streets lined with pine trees. The town had four schools with 5,700 students, an enclosed sports complex, and a swimming pool. Among the main buildings in town were the *Energetik* Palace of Culture and the *Prometey* cinema. The *Yupiter* radio factory provided some jobs. The average age of residents of the town was twenty-six. Pripyat was the Soviet equivalent of an American company town: the white reactor halls and turbines of the Chernobyl plant on its skyline were a reminder that the town had been built for one purpose. The 49,000 people of Pripyat and three surrounding villages had planned to spend the May Day holiday with family outings, gardening, trips to the Pripyat River, or at home watching the Red Square Parade on television. Schools had arranged May Day festivities. Workers looked forward to duck shooting on the Pripyat Marshes. Housewives had arranged special family meals. But those plans had been abandoned.

On May Day, Pripyat was a ghost town. Parks, gardens and sandpits were deserted. Offices, shops, schools were locked. There was no sign of life in any of the town's apartments. No radios or televisions played: no lights burned in its windows at night. The town had been hurriedly abandoned. Washing flapped unattended on clothes lines, children's toys lay discarded, apartments left in disarray. Windows and exterior doors had been taped up, and the apartment blocks had been locked by officials. One of the only buildings showing lights was the Communist Party committee building which, according to a journalist from the Soviet news agency *Novosti*, was full of crates of rubber protective suits and masks.

Pripyat's residents, evacuated four days earlier by a fleet of 1,216 Kiev city buses and 300 trucks, were scattered across the rural countryside west of the Chernobyl plant and in other parts of the Ukraine. They were living in cramped conditions in hastily-arranged billets at farms and villages. In some areas, two evacuees had been allocated to every household. Ukrainian party officials worked long hours to feed, shelter and comfort the evacuees. Many had fled without so much as a change of clothing. Families had become separated, and people did not know of the whereabouts of their close relatives or children. Almost a month after the accident, *Pravda* reported that some people were still trying to locate relatives.[7] Ten thousand Pripyat children, including 3,000 infants, had been taken directly to vacation camps in the Ukraine and other Soviet republics. Some of the children were suffering psychological disturbances caused by separation from their parents, the upheaval of leaving home and fear of radiation. Doctors and nurses monitored them closely.

For the most part, aside from police and military patrols, Pripyat was empty on May Day. But not quite. Two elderly women, frightened of being taken from their homes, had ignored loudspeaker appeals to board the buses and evaded the police patrols. Anastasia Semenyaka, aged eighty-five, and Maria Karpenok, aged seventy-four, were hiding in their apartment. They were found only after thirty-four days. They had survived in the ghost town by eating tinned food and drinking bottled water. Eventually, they were taken to hospital. There was no information on the dosage of radiation they had received.

Ten miles to the southeast of the stricken power plant, at the ancient regional centre of Chernobyl, there was still some air of normality on May Day. A small and sleepy place with a population of 12,500 people, the town had long been surpassed in size by Pripyat. Chernobyl was a port for barges on the Pripyat River and the site of the repair works of the Dnieper River steamship company, as well as of pig iron, cheese and animal feed factories. It had four schools, a hospital and a cinema with a wide screen. The local newspaper was called *The Banner of Victory*. Like Pripyat, Chernobyl was located at the eastern edge of the Byelorussian-Ukrainian Woodlands. It was a recreation area.

On May Day, many people in Chernobyl behaved as if nothing untoward had happened. Others had shut themselves in their homes while they waited to hear if they were to be evacuated. Children were forbidden to go outside. Families crowded round to listen to the radio.

Rumours abounded and people were afraid. A Soviet ham radio operator from an area south of the plant was later reported to have told an Israeli ham that he knew there were at least 600–700 casualties from the Chernobyl accident and that sixty people were dead. As it turned out, the report was wildly exaggerated, but it is reasonable to assume that people in the town of Chernobyl had heard similar rumours.

On May Day, the town of Chernobyl had not yet been evacuated; officials said that radiation levels did not warrant it. Like the people of Pripyat, residents of Chernobyl town had been slow to waken to the scale of the nuclear emergency. (A Soviet journalist who visited the Pripyat area just after the accident reported that weddings were still being celebrated.) But as the days passed, as reports came of the evacuation of Pripyat, as army vehicles and decontamination teams passed through the town, nervousness must have mounted in Chernobyl and in other villages which had not yet been evacuated. Some people fled.

Chernobyl had become the headquarters of the emergency accident commission set up by the Soviet Government headed by Soviet Deputy Prime Minister Boris Shcherbina, a young-looking sixty-six-year-old with a reputation for energy and organising drive. On May Day, the commission was operating out of the party headquarters in Chernobyl. On its doors were pinned handwritten signs announcing the location of the representatives of the Academy of Sciences, the Ministry of Power and Electrification, the Ministry of Health and other agencies. Party officials, scientists and engineers had flown in hurriedly from Moscow and other centres to staff the emergency operation. Trucks loaded with cement, building supplies and decontamination materials were converging on Chernobyl from Kiev, Chernigov, Zhitomir, Cherkassy, Dnepropetrovsk and many other areas. The atmosphere at Chernobyl was described by two *Pravda* correspondents as 'tense.' One official at the party headquarters said: 'The atmosphere reigning here is reminiscent of the headquarters of an army waging an offensive.'

Officials in the Ukrainian capital of Kiev, eighty miles to the south of Chernobyl, were helping to coordinate the relocation of the tens of thousands of evacuees. The lights burned throughout the night on every floor of the Ukrainian Ministry of Health which oversaw the work of more than 1,300 doctors and medical workers. The medical teams were operating near the Chernobyl plant and at evacuation centres throughout the Ukraine, giving aid to victims of radiation and performing medical checks on the evacuees. Four workers from the Chernobyl power plant who had been seriously irradiated in the first hours after the accident were being treated at Kiev's Roentgenology, Radiology, and Oncology Scientific Research Institute. But the majority of people who needed treatment were suffering from problems which had nothing to do with radiation exposure. They were suffering from stress caused by the emotional upheaval of leaving their homes and being separated from their children and other relatives.

Thousands of foreign students studying in Kiev were worried. The Soviet media said that there was no radiation danger to the city's 2.5 million residents. But the students heard a different story from Western radio broadcasts. The short-wave broadcasts, which were jammed in the Soviet Union and hard to pick up, relayed advice to stay inside, to wash vegetables and fruit and to drink only bottled water. They also relayed reports from Western Europe and the United States which suggested that the Chernobyl accident was serious. Hank Birnbaum, the American leader of a group of students studying at the Foreign Language Institute in Kiev, later told reporters: 'We felt caught between two worlds. On the one hand the Soviets were saying nothing, and from the West there was a flood of information, some of it exaggerated.'

Hundreds of foreign students, businessmen and tourists left the Ukraine over the May Day period. Groups of British students were evacuated from Kiev and the Byelorussian capital of Minsk at the advice of the British Government. Finnish and West German workers employed on projects in the area left, too. Checks in Helsinki showed that the seventy-two Finns evacuated from Kiev had traces of radioactive iodine in their thyroid glands, but the Finnish Office of Nuclear Radiation Safety said the levels were 'in no way alarming.' A West German machinery executive said on his arrival in Frankfurt: 'Local people were totally in the dark. Life was normal in Kiev.' Another German said: 'The whole city was all dressed for May Day this morning when we left.'

Karen Weisblatt, a twenty-six-year-old language graduate from Chicago, had taken the overnight train to Moscow after she received a telegram from the United States that ordered: 'Leave Kiev immediately. Discontinue course.

Water contaminated by radiation. Major nuclear melt-down at Chernobyl. Moscow water safe . . . fly out as soon as possible. Love Mother.' In Moscow, Soviet officials ran a geiger counter over British students who had fled Kiev and pronounced them clean. But when they arrived in London, traces of radiation were found on their clothing and the clothing was destroyed.

A Soviet television reporter interviewed two British tourists in Moscow on May Day before they flew home. A transcript of the interview threw into sharp relief the situation in which foreign visitors found themselves:

> *Soviet correspondent:* I had a meeting with British tourists outside the *Rossiya* Hotel during the festive merry-making. Jim Tweedle, a railway dispatcher from Glasgow, and Ian Smith, a Devon businessman, were on a tour around our country that was organised by the Thomson Holidays tourist company . . .
>
> *Jim Tweedle:* We had a very fine and pleasant trip, a trip that none of us will forget. Everything was wonderful until we were brought back to Moscow yesterday.
>
> *Soviet correspondent:* I asked them the reason for their unexpected return.
>
> *Ian Smith:* Suddenly a representative of Thomson Holidays told us that an atomic explosion had allegedly taken place in the Soviet Union. The city of Kiev had been evacuated. Many people have died and thousands have been injured. We were also told that our lives are in danger and that we must immediately leave Moscow.
>
> *Soviet correspondent:* That is not true. The situation in Kiev is normal. People there are also celebrating May Day, just as they are in Moscow . . .
>
> *Ian Smith:* I also asked the Thomson Holiday repre-sentatives about this but they were unable to give me a sensible explanation. One gains the impression that it is only Thomson Holidays that is suddenly so concerned and has been exaggerating all this.
>
> *Soviet correspondent:* I see. It is a provocation.[8]

Ukrainians and Byelorussians listening to Soviet broadcasts on May Day, or reading the official Soviet newspapers, learned almost nothing about the Chernobyl accident. Three official statements, the first appearing three days after the accident, had not described the accident, explained how it happened, revealed how much radiation had been released, or detailed the extent or nature of injuries caused by the accident. The Soviet people knew only that two people had been killed initially, and that 197 people had been sent to hospital. It was only after the May Day parades were over that the Soviet Council of Ministers issued another brief statement. This statement indicated that eighteen of the people injured in the nuclear disaster were in a serious condition.

This is the English language text of the statement, as carried by the Tass news agency:

From the Council of Ministers of the USSR

Moscow, May 1 (Tass) – Efforts to implement a complex of technical measures continued at the Chernobyl nuclear power station (NPS) in the duration of April 30th. The radioactivity on the territory of the NPS and the NPS' settlement dropped 1.5–2 times. Work is under way to deactivate the contaminated areas adjacent to the NPS territory. Medical assistance is being administered to those affected of whom eighteen people are in a serious condition. There are no foreign citizens among those affected.

The eighteen people were firemen and plant operators who had fought to control the burning nuclear reactor. On May Day, they were in Moscow's Hospital Number Six where they were suffering from radiation sickness. Some had inhaled or swallowed burning radioactive particles. Their hair was falling out, and their skin was peeling off. Some had suffered intestinal damage. Doctors already knew that most of them were going to die. Scores of other victims of the accident were also in the hospital. Many of them would die, too.

The Soviet people heard nothing about the life-and-death battle that was going on at the Moscow hospital. The media appeared more preoccupied with a big bicycle race than Chernobyl. It gave a lot of coverage to the thirty-ninth annual *Mir* (Peace) amateur cycling race due to start from Kiev's Square of the October Revolution in a few days' time. Like the Western students, Ukrainians wanting to learn more about the situation at Chernobyl tuned in to what they call 'the voices' – the short-wave radio broadcasts of the American *Radio Liberty*, the *Voice of America* and the BBC. What they heard was disturbing.

The first signs of alarm began to appear in Kiev over the May Day holiday. Large numbers of Kiev's citizens decided to get out of the city, and extra cashiers had to be put on duty at the city's railway station to cope with the long queues at the ticket stalls. Long lines also appeared at *Aeroflot* offices. But most Kiev people seemed unworried. They streamed into the centre of the city to watch the May Day Parade. People in the Byelorussian capital of Minsk, a city of one and a half million people about 170 miles north of the Chernobyl plant, also turned out for their May Day parade.

In Kiev, 120,000 people marched through the main street, *Kreshchatic*, led by senior members of the Ukrainian Communist Party and World War Two veterans. The marchers carried flowers, apple blossom and banners. Dancers in Ukrainian folk costume made a colourful sight. The parade was reviewed by a member of the Politburo, Vladimir Shcherbitsky, the head of the Ukrainian Communist Party. The slogans carried by the marchers stressed the Soviet Union's love of peace and support for Soviet foreign policy. Collective farms from around Kiev displayed their produce on stalls. The crowds were in a holiday mood. The crowds bought icecream, *piroshki* pancakes and fruit juice from street vendors. It was a sunny day and the city's chestnut trees were in blossom.

The nation-wide evening television news programme, *Vremya*, began with its usual shot of a clock ticking away the last seconds before 9 p.m. It was followed by the programme logo – a stylised globe, a glowing red star and a white line depicting an orbiting satellite. 'Good evening,' said the woman announcer. 'Hello, comrades,' said the male anchorman. The programme briefly reported the statement about Chernobyl from the Council of Ministers. It also devoted three minutes to film of the May Day celebrations in the Ukraine.

*   *   *

The story was different in Western Europe. On May Day, there was fear that at times threatened to spill over into hysteria.

Across West Germany, city parks and sandpits were empty. In Austria, mothers warned their children to stay away from puddles of rainwater. In Denmark, police ran geiger counters over trucks returning from the Kiev region. In Britain, officials checked fresh milk. In Sweden, farmers were advised to bring their cows in from the fields. Across Europe, frightened people swamped government offices, hospitals and pharmacies seeking advice about radioactive fallout. Authorities in many countries conducted frequent analyses of air, soil, plants, water and milk. Radiation counters showed levels of radioactivity up to fifteen times the normal background rates. In some areas, readings were hundreds of times above normal.[9]

On May Day, Western reporters wrote stories speculating about thousands of deaths near the Chernobyl nuclear power plant. There was talk of the reactor blazing out of control and melting down. There were reports that the fire had spread to a second reactor and that it, too, was melting down. A Swedish analyst said US satellite pictures showed 'two bright red spots visible beneath a cloud of blueish smoke.'

Europeans became compulsive in their attention to radio

and television broadcasts as they searched for news of the nuclear accident near a small town in the Ukraine which no one had heard of until three days previously. They listened to weather forecasts to find out if their homes were in the path of the radioactive plumes which were drifting high in the atmosphere, wandering at the will of the winds over a 2,000-mile arc from Finland to Italy.

Around May Day, the radioactive plumes, which had initially blown across the Ukraine, Byelorussia, the Soviet Baltic republics, Poland and Scandinavia, altered direction and began to drift across south-eastern France, Switzerland, southern Germany, Austria, Czechoslovakia and Hungary. The plumes headed for Britain. Heavy rainfall washed the radioactive particles from the skies and deposited them on Bavarian towns, Carinthian villages, Yugoslav cities, French mountains and Swiss lakes. The pattern of deposition was uneven and depended crucially on where the rain fell. The West German city of Munich recorded high radiation levels after a thunderstorm on the eve of May Day. Inspectors were called in to make geiger counter checks on fruit and vegetables in the city's famous outdoor *Viktualienmarkt*. The plumes contained at least twenty radionuclides – products of the gutted reactor core – including iodine^{131}, caesium^{137}, strontium^{90}, zirconium^{95}, ruthenium^{103} and tellurium^{134}. There were also traces of plutonium.

The radionuclides began decaying as soon as they were released. Some would be dangerous for a few minutes or days; others would remain dangerous for months or many years. The quick-decaying radionuclides released the most intense radiation, while the slow-decaying ones would continue to produce lower-level radiation for some time to come. The hazard the radionuclides presented depended on their half-life. Half-life refers to the time needed for one-half of the radioactive material to decay. Plutonium^{239} has a half-life of 24,400 years.

Experts warned that exposure to even small doses of radioactivity carried health hazards. Europeans learned that anyone who breathed or ingested radioactive materials had a heightened long-term risk of contracting cancer and there was danger of genetic damage. Radiation experts had already begun to make grim predictions of how many would die of cancer in Europe as a result of Chernobyl. The numbers ranged from a few dozen to several thousand. The meteorological charts that showed where the wind blew and where the rain fell across Europe amounted to what one Western scientist described as a 'cancer map.'[10]

Public health officials in Europe and Scandinavia were most immediately concerned about fallout of radioactive iodine[131]. Radioactive iodine, which dissolves in rainwater, collects in the thyroid gland in the neck. The exposure route is through contaminated milk, but it can also be inhaled. Experts said babies and infants were particularly vulnerable to iodine[131] because their thyroid glands are smaller than those of adults. On May Day, Polish doctors were completing a massive exercise to give ten million children protective doses of a bitter brown iodine liquid called *lugol* (dubbed 'Russian Coca-Cola' by the Poles). The iodine in the liquid blocks the absorption of radioactive iodine because it fills all available sites in the thyroid. The radioactive iodine cannot then be absorbed and it is excreted.

Other radioactive materials presented a danger because they had fallen on crops and pastures. Public health officials worried about the long-term dangers of caesium[137]. This isotope settled as radioactive dust on the outer leaves of vegetables and plants. The officials warned that caesium could enter the food chain if livestock consumed contaminated grass or plants. Austrians, Poles and Scandinavians were warned to wash fresh fruit and vegetables. Sweden, Denmark and Norway ordered a ban on imports of food – including meat, vegetables, potatoes and fish – from the Soviet Union and East European countries. Polish officials advised people to take regular showers and to wash their hair frequently.

A United Press International story reported ground-level radiation readings fifteen times normal in Sweden, twice normal rates in Denmark, atmospheric radiation between two and ten times normal at high altitudes above Switzerland, an 'insignificant' radiation increase in France, between one to one and a half and two times the normal atmospheric radiation in Italy. Britain's National Radiological Protection Board reported no increase in normal levels of radiation in the atmosphere. In most areas of Europe, the health risk was negligible, but few people knew how to interpret the radiation readings which were being reported. Some radiation readings were much higher. United Press International quoted a Polish radiation expert as saying that radiation levels in most areas of Poland were fifty to one hundred times higher than normal and that one area – Mikolajki in north-eastern Poland – had recorded levels 500 times normal three days previously. Inhabitants of the village were reported to have taken in a bigger dose of radiation just by breathing than hospital X-ray staff were permitted to absorb in a year. Mikolajki was one of the worst of the radioactive 'hot spots' scattered across Europe. In some places only a field or a road separated high areas of radioactivity from areas that recorded negligible levels. The deposition patterns depended on where the spring rains fell.

The anxieties of Europeans were deepened by the near-silence from Moscow. People were angered and bewildered by the fact that the Soviet Union had not announced the accident until three days after it had occurred and then only after Swedish officials had reported unusual levels of radioactivity in the atmosphere at the Forsmark Nuclear Power Station sixty miles north of Stockholm.

Even after the first terse announcement on April 28th, most of the basic questions remained unanswered. What sort of accident was it? How did it happen? Was the death toll really only two? How much radioactivity had escaped? What danger remained? These were the questions being asked by worried Europeans. Subsequent Soviet statements on the accident had done nothing to calm their fears.

Anxiety was compounded by the nature of radioactivity, an insidious poison that cannot be seen, tasted or smelled. Radiation was identified in many people's minds with the destructive power of nuclear weapons and the other great fear of the twentieth century, cancer. Europeans, brought up in an atomic age, showed remarkable ignorance of the nature of radioactivity. People struggled to understand the jargon of radiation experts: isotopes, becquerels, half-lives, meltdowns, roentgens, millirems, containment vessels, sieverts, rems and rads. Senior officials of the European atomic energy industry and radiation biology experts were under siege to give interviews to television reporters or to appear in radio phone-in shows.

'I am a mother of small children. What measures should I take against radiation damage to my children?' 'I am pregnant. Should I have an abortion?' 'Is it safe to hang washing on the line?' These were some of the questions asked of the radiation experts. One pregnant woman in West Germany spent May Day preparing to fly to New Zealand to have her child (she later gave birth to a healthy baby). In Poland, there was anger and bitter humour. A Warsaw father, a technician in his thirties, said: 'Can you imagine? Telling no one. They are bandits, madmen.' A woman clerk in a small Polish neighbourhood food stores commented: 'Sure, go ahead, drink the milk. Haven't you heard? Everything's fine. It's all under control. The milk is from Red cows.' Another Pole said: 'Nothing good ever blew on a wind from the East.' A report prepared for the Rainbow Group of the European Parliament later estimated that accepted radiation norms were exceeded in areas inhabited by thirty-five per cent of the Polish people.[11]

The confusion of Europeans was heightened by the conflicting advice given by officials at national, regional and local levels and by the lack of coordination. Officials were guided by conflicting considerations. They were worried about the need to limit health hazards from radiation, while at the same time trying to calm people's fears and prevent panic. But another consideration also played a part: a desire to keep domestic political and economic damage from the Chernobyl accident to a minimum. Across Europe, leaders of the nuclear industry were playing down the accident for fear of a backlash against nuclear power; environmentalist groups, such as the Greens party in West Germany, argued that the accident would have severe environmental and health impact.

The result was chaos. People in some parts of West Germany were told that milk and vegetables were completely safe, while in others they were advised to buy frozen and canned foods and to avoid fresh milk. In Belgium, farmers in Flanders were told to keep their cows inside but not in Wallonia. In Britain, environmental organisations were flooded with phone calls, suggesting that people did not trust official information. Bewildered Europeans were assured that nuclear energy was safe, while at the same time they were told not to eat spinach, lettuce and peaches, not to pick flowers or mushrooms, to keep their children out of open-air swimming pools, even to take showers after being out in the rain. Nuclear industry officials made contrasts between safe nuclear energy in the West, and unsafe nuclear energy in the East. What were Europeans to make of all this? One West German commented: 'I really do not know what to do any more because I've been listening to the radio every hour.'

On a visit to the Indonesian island of Bali, en route to a summit in Tokyo of seven Western leaders, US President Ronald Reagan said he had been in touch with Soviet General Secretary Mikhail Gorbachev about the accident, but that details about what happened were sparse. Reagan said, 'We're trying to keep track of what's going on over there, but we're limited in our knowledge.' British Prime Minister Margaret Thatcher said Soviet secrecy over the Chernobyl accident showed that the West must insist on strict verification on arms control and her foreign secretary, Sir Geoffrey Howe, criticised Moscow for a 'lack in European good-neighbourliness', an apparent reference to one of the slogans at the Moscow May Day Parade which called on the 'Peoples of Europe' to 'struggle for peaceful cooperation and good-neighbourly relations among states . . .' Someone at the Foreign Office had been reading *Pravda*.

What else did Europeans learn from their radios, newspapers, news agencies and televisions on May Day? They were told that a Dutch amateur cycling team pulled out of the Kiev cycle race because of fears of radiation. The London Festival Ballet postponed a trip to the Soviet Union. Members of the *Dynamo-Kiev* soccer team, who were in France for the Cupwinners' Cup Final against *Atletico Madrid* in Lyon, tried for eight hours without success to telephone their families in the Ukraine.

In Bonn, a West German nuclear executive described how an excited and upset Soviet diplomat rushed into his office and asked for advice after calling the Chernobyl nuclear accident 'a terrible catastrophe.' Manfred Petroll of the Atom Forum, an industry-backed lobby group that promotes the use of nuclear energy, identified the Soviet official as A. I. Chagaev, the Soviet Embassy's science and technology officer. Petroll said Chagaev 'was looking upset.' He and Atom Forum director Peter Haug talked with Chagaev for two hours, while at the same time telephoning many West German nuclear experts. Chagaev sometimes grabbed the phone himself to ask questions. Chagaev said he had been instructed to find out about graphite fires, but that Moscow had provided no specific details about the accident. A story from the Associated Press reported that Soviet officials had asked Swedish authorities if Stockholm's Karolinska Hospital was prepared to receive people suffering from radiation sickness from the area of the Chernobyl accident. The story was denied by a Swedish Foreign Ministry spokesman within a few hours. A hospital spokeswoman confessed she had been mistaken. But by then the story was running.

In West Germany, a daily newspaper in the town of Bergisch Gladbach quoted one of a party of a hundred German tourists who flew from Moscow to Kiev on the day of the nuclear accident as saying they suddenly saw a 'black cloud in a bright blue sky' from the aircraft at around 3 p.m. Herbert Hopf, retired, said the *Aeroflot* plane was at a height of about 10,000 feet when he saw a cloud 'shaped like a Christmas tree, or the tip of a ragged mountain range.' Another member of the party said that on arriving at Kiev airport, 'It was like night, with the sky torn by lightning. We heard several explosions.'

The unease of Europeans was heightened by alarming statements from government officials and Western nuclear scientists. A group of US senators was quoted as saying that up to 2,000 people might have died in the Chernobyl disaster. US Secretary of State George Shultz said he believed casualties were far higher than the Soviet Union had reported. Paul Leventhal, director of the US Nuclear Control Institute, was quoted as saying that the Soviet authorities should consider evacuating Kiev's 2.5 million people as a precaution. 'Kiev would probably have to be evacuated. A precautionary evacuation has to be considered at this time,' he said. Theodore Taylor, a physicist who served on the US Presidential commission that investigated the 1979 nuclear power plant accident at Three Mile Island, Pennsylvania, was quoted as saying that cancer deaths caused by fallout from Chernobyl could exceed the short-term death toll from the bombing of Hiroshima, assuming most of the radioactivity from the reactor had been released. He said the amount of strontium[90] and caesium[137] in the Chernobyl reactor was equal to that produced by a thirty-megaton bomb blast.

Western reporters contributed to the growing hysteria over Chernobyl with this sort of reporting. The director-general of the International Atomic Energy Agency, Hans Blix, later concluded: 'Soviet reporting was late, meagre, but not untrue. The Western reporting was fast, massive and often very misleading, notably in casualty figures.'[12]

The most notorious example was a report from a Moscow correspondent of United Press International which quoted a Kiev woman as saying in a telephone conversation that the nuclear power plant disaster had claimed 2,000 lives and that many more people had been sent to hospital with radiation sickness. She was quoted as saying: 'The whole October Hospital is packed with people who suffer from radiation sickness . . . the people were not buried in ordinary cemeteries but in the village of Pirogov, where radioactive wastes are usually buried.' One report carried by newspapers quoted a Dutch radio ham as saying he monitored a ham radio broadcast apparently emanating from the Soviet Union which told of 'many hundreds dead and wounded.' The Dutch ham said he had been told two nuclear reactors at Chernobyl had melted down and were burning.

Western journalists also made hopeless blunders. A few days after May Day an Italian television report showed what it claimed was a videotape taken by a Yugoslav tourist of the Chernobyl nuclear plant. The building shown in the film was, in reality, a cement factory in Trieste. But it was inevitable that the Western media would make mistakes. Given the Soviet secrecy, and the refusal to allow Western reporters anywhere near the stricken reactor, Western journalists had to read backward from the evidence. Reporters were at the mercy of the information which people gave them. The Soviet refusal to disclose more information encouraged reporters to invite experts on nuclear power to engage in speculation about the accident. Reporters also encouraged experts to speculate on the extent of environmental damage to croplands in the Ukraine, one of the Soviet Union's most important farming regions. Prices on commodity markets rose amid speculation that radioactive contamination could force the Soviet Union to increase imports of grains, sugar and dairy products. 'The market is going through the roof,' said Bill Demaria, an economist with the London-based International Wheat Council.

Soviet officials were angered by the Western exaggeration of the Chernobyl accident. They described the reports of thousands of casualties, mass graves for the dead and

poisoned croplands as malicious and lying anti-Soviet propaganda. *Izvestia* accused 'imperialist circles' of seizing on
the accident at Chernobyl 'as an argument against the at-
tainment of realistic accords with the Soviet Union on curbing
the arms race and eliminating the threat of nuclear missile
war.' *Tass* correspondent A. Lyuty wrote in an article in
Sovetskaya Rossiya that the anti-Soviet campaign 'is beat-
ing all records for hypocrisy and inhumanity'. Lyuty said:

> Washington – For more than a week now a map of the
> world has appeared on US television screens almost
> every hour. That map shows the whole of Western
> Europe as a thick red blob. Before the viewers' eyes that
> blob spreads to Asia, engulfing more and more countries
> . . . These blobs, of course, are products of the imagina-
> tion of the TV companies' anti-Sovietists and all manner
> of consultants from the Reagan administration. When
> Americans need a good scare with 'the Soviet threat,' the
> producers of such shows splash out the red paint . . . you
> can understand why some people living in the western
> states of California, Oregon and Washington, seeing
> these horrors on television, immediately rush out to the
> local pharmacies to buy iodine solution and are now
> scouring the stores in search of special protective suits.[13]

Soviet spokesmen in the West disclosed more to Western
audiences than officials at home told their own people. But
this did not deflect Western criticism. Anger in Western
Europe at the lack of information and apparent indifference to safety standards prompted some of the harshest and
most fundamental criticism of the Soviet Union for many
years. Western newspapers assailed the Soviet Union for its
secrecy on Chernobyl and for failing to live up to its pledges
under the 1975 Helsinki accords to abide by the principle of
a 'free flow of information.' Comparisons were made with
the Soviet Union's stonewalling after its air force shot down
a South Korean airliner with 269 people aboard in September, 1983. *The Economist* commented:

Distrust the Kremlin's count. The world's worst nuclear accident may have killed scores of people already. Hundreds, perhaps thousands, will probably die from cancer and other delayed effects into the next century. Outrageously, the precise nature of the accident, and therefore the scope of the human tragedy, can still only be guessed at; Mr Gorbachev's much-bally-hooed flair for public relations did not dispose him to warn Sweden that a cloud of poisonous radiation was drifting its way.

The London *Daily Mirror* editorialised:

The Soviet Union . . . seeks the help of the West in putting out its nuclear fire but denies to it the information which might help it to safeguard its own people . . . The fact that it cares nothing for those beyond its borders will be remembered long after the name of the Chernobyl power station has been forgotten.

French and German newspapers saw the Chernobyl disaster as the result of a secretive and authoritarian Soviet system making decisions without involving the people whose lives it rules. The Munich newspaper *Süddeutsche Zeitung* said: 'The Russians keep pointing out that we have to live with them. They also have to live with us.' The left-wing French newspaper, *Liberation*, commented: 'Communists make electricity like they make war – without worrying too much about victims and eliminating observers.' The Stockholm daily, *Svenska Dagbladet*, said that Soviet society was 'far too primitive to use a sophisticated technique like nuclear power.' *The New York Times* commented, under a headline *Mayday! and May Day*, 'If the Soviet Union has a closed, arrogant nuclear industry disdainful of safety precautions, the stifling of internal debate may be in large part to blame. A closed society, where only the highest circles are permitted to debate, hears only its own voice.'

Another comment came about a week after the accident

in a cyclostyled information sheet issued by the underground Polish organisation *Kos*. It detailed the health
and environmental damage in Poland as a result of the
Chernobyl disaster. The unknown author concluded:

> So, there you are. In the Ukraine an enormous
> tragedy; in the whole of Europe an ecological catas-
> trophe. What is happening in Moscow, which is respon-
> sible for it?
> Well, in Moscow, they're having a parade . . .[14]

2

THE SECRET DISASTER

You expected from us too much too soon.

Georgy Arbatov, director of the Soviet Institute
for Study of the United States and Canada[1]

For Mikhail Gorbachev and the new leadership team on top of Lenin's Tomb on May Day, 1986, the unfolding disaster at Chernobyl was their first full-blown crisis. It was also the first serious test of Gorbachev's promise to provide the Soviet people with more information. He had called his new policy *glasnost* – openness.

In his first thirteen months of power, Gorbachev had encouraged Soviet officialdom to be more candid and frank and had urged the Soviet media to report more honestly about problems and failures in Soviet society. He had given people more access to information. He had opened the door to a debate of economic, environmental and social issues. He had loosened censorship in the arts. His new policy was like a breath of oxygen for the Soviet people. At last, their closed society seemed to be opening up. Then the No. 4 reactor at Chernobyl blew up in the early hours of April 26th. The accident tested the policy of *glasnost* in a way that it had not been tested before. The policy, or at least the policy-makers, failed the test. In their initial response to Chernobyl, the Soviet leadership betrayed the principles of *glasnost*. There was no openness from the Soviet Union on May Day. There was only near-silence and secrecy.

It took Moscow almost three days to announce the

accident. Even then, at a time when the nuclear accident was not yet under control, Soviet officials continued to insist that there was nothing to worry about and that radiation posed a negligible risk. It was not until May 14th – eighteen days after the accident – that Gorbachev appeared on national television to talk about the disaster. It was not until about five weeks after the No. 4 reactor blew up that the Soviet Union began telling its own people and the world details of the Chernobyl accident and its consequences.

Westerners found the Soviet silence incomprehensible. Why did the Soviet Union go ahead with the May Day parades, particularly in Kiev, in a holiday-as-usual atmosphere? How was it possible to reconcile the image of a smiling Gorbachev on top of Lenin's Tomb with the reality of a nuclear reactor in a perilous state? Why did the Soviet media seem more preoccupied with a bicycle race than with Chernobyl? Why had Gorbachev failed to live up to his promise of *glasnost*? People in the West were disappointed. They had been encouraged by the reports that Gorbachev represented a refreshing new style of Soviet leadership. They had learned from their newspapers and televisions that Gorbachev was behind the exciting changes in the Soviet Union. Yet initially, Moscow responded to Chernobyl in a time-worn fashion – by falling back on habits of secrecy and denial. Was Gorbachev any different from his predecessors? Had anything changed in the Soviet Union?

*   *   *

The first time the name Mikhail Gorbachev meant anything to most people in the West was in December, 1984, when he flew to London as the head of a Soviet parliamentary delegation. It was not Gorbachev's first visit to the West. In 1983, he had visited Canada, where he wore a black cowboy hat and grinned like a Russian version of J.R. from *Dallas*. And in 1984, he visited Italy to attend the funeral of Enrico Berlinguer, the iconoclastic chairman of the Italian Communist Party, a man whom many in

Moscow saw as a traitor to Communism. But the London trip was different: though Gorbachev had not yet moved into the top role in the Soviet Union he was the front-runner to replace the feeble and ineffective Konstantin Chernenko when Chernenko's emphysema finally brought him down. In fact, when Yuri Andropov died earlier in the year, it had been widely thought that Gorbachev might well assume the leadership. By December, it was clear that Chernenko's days were numbered and that Gorbachev was the man most likely to succeed. So the attention of the world was focused on him.

From the moment he stepped off his plane at Heathrow Airport, his official engagements were dogged by a pack of journalists. It was clear that Gorbachev was the first Kremlin politician to recognise the importance of image projection in an age of mass media politics. The old-line Savile Row tailoring establishment of Gieves and Hawke had let it be known – discreetly, of course – that they were responsible for Gorbachev's well-turned-out look. Raisa Gorbachev made her own headlines with a shopping spree in London's Bond Street, where she was said to have used an American Express card for her purchases. After a meeting at Number 10 Downing Street, Prime Minister Margaret Thatcher said that Gorbachev was a man with whom she could do business.

It was all like a visit by a ranking Western politician, except for a side trip to the decayed inner-city London neighbourhood of Clerkenwell Green – a site not on most tourist itineraries. It was an important stopover, for it was in Clerkenwell Green that Vladimir Ilyich Lenin, living in exile, had passed his time reading and writing in a building that is now a minor shrine in the Communist pantheon. While in Britain, Gorbachev did more than call on other politicians. He wanted to look at British industry. He visited a car plant where he was photographed behind the wheel of a car on the assembly line. And he flew north to Scotland for talks with major engineering firms. The visit was cut short by the death of Marshal Ustinov, the defence minister. Before his hurried return to Moscow for the funeral rites, it seemed apparent that Gorbachev was not a man of the same mould as previous Soviet leaders. Western commentators even described him as a Soviet version of John F. Kennedy. But after nearly a year of the Gorbachev era, there was still no way to assess how the new leader would react when he was faced with a real challenge.

Gorbachev's first year in office had been a relatively peaceful time, with no major international difficulties. It was the Americans who seemed to be taking the beatings on the international front. Less than two weeks earlier, an American air raid on Libya had triggered anti-American demonstrations in West European capitals and condemnations at the United Nations. And the new leader had been showing a much more open face to the West on the question of arms control, where skilful diplomacy had begun to make the Americans look like the sole perpetrators of the arms race. The new leadership in Moscow had come to power bringing with them high expectations for change: after all, they were a new generation of leaders, ready to make the break from the decline and decay of the Brezhnev years, a break many had hoped for when Yuri Andropov took over but which Andropov had been unable to deliver in his short-lived term of office. But suddenly, with the western press and electronic media in full cry over the radioactive cloud that continued to spew forth from the Chernobyl reactor, the course ahead was suddenly not so smooth, or clear.

What many people in the West forgot during the early days of the new regime was just how desperate was the need for drastic change in the Soviet Union. But it was clear to Mikhail Gorbachev. Even before he moved to the top of the Soviet hierarchy in March 1985, he had signalled that as leader, he would move on three main fronts: the need to open up Soviet society, the imperative to reduce the power of a politically-selected management bureaucracy and the absolute necessity finally to throw off from the neck of the Soviet economy the death grip of Josef Stalin's industrial model. The reason for this three-pronged attack was simple: to Gorbachev and the men who had put him at the top of the leadership, drastic reform was the only solution to the basic problems of the Soviet economy.

Above all, Gorbachev seemed determined to shake Soviet society out of its habit of secrecy. It was clear to him that the Soviet Union could not start to tackle its economic and management troubles if it continued to conceal and even refuse to acknowledge them. He wanted to throw a spotlight on areas of Soviet life that were hidden in darkness. His aim was to dispel inertia and complacency and to stimulate the creativity and initiative which he saw as necessary for the economic development of the country.

This ambition lay behind his new policy of *glasnost*. The word is usually translated as openness or transparency. But it does not imply freedom of speech in a Western sense. Nor does it mean a new Western-style attitude to reporting. *Glasnost* was a political weapon to shake up sluggish administrators and officials and to overcome bureaucratic opposition to economic and political reforms. Gorbachev wanted to cast more light on the official decision-making process; to air certain subjects that had previously been taboo; and to ensure that some negative information and unpalatable facts would be published.

The Chernobyl disaster confronted the new Soviet leadership with a crisis that was a set-piece illustration of the economic, political and personnel problems that Gorbachev wanted to overcome with his new policy of *glasnost*. And, initially, the Soviet leadership reacted to the accident in the old way – by not talking about it.

*　　*　　*

As with Conan Doyle's dog that did not bark, the mystery of Chernobyl was an event that did not happen – namely, a Soviet warning to the world that the nuclear reactor had blown up. To many Europeans, this Soviet behaviour suggested indifference, even callousness. But this was not the case. Publicly, Moscow may have stone-walled in the face of Western criticism. Privately, it was clear that Soviet officials were appalled and embarrassed by Chernobyl.

The lack of warning about the accident was probably motivated in part by practical calculations. The respected British fortnightly publication, *Soviet Analyst*, argued that if the Soviet Union had immediately disclosed the accident, and if Gorbachev had appeared on television to explain what had happened, many people in the Ukraine and Byelorussia might have taken fright, and the result would have been mass panic.[2] The Soviet people were not accustomed to seeing their leaders announcing bad news, and assurances from Gorbachev would probably not have been believed. The Soviet leadership may have calculated that more people would have been killed or injured in panic than would have been harmed by radiation. If, say, inhabitants had fled in panic from Kiev and Minsk, the two largest cities near Chernobyl, the death toll in road accidents alone could have been high. One nightmare possibility was an uncontrolled exodus through areas that had been contaminated by radiation. The need to prevent panic is clearly one reason why the Soviet Union was at pains to show a façade of normality on May Day.

Who can be confident that Western politicians would not be guided by similar calculations in the event of a nuclear accident in Western Europe or the United States? Under any system, governments are not inclined to tell their people unpleasant truths. But Gorbachev was able to maintain the façade of normality because he did not have the problem of awkward journalists trying to discover the truth about Chernobyl. The Soviet media are under state control and journalists are expected to act as allies, not adversaries, of the state.

Officially, the explanation that has been offered for the silence is that Moscow did not learn of the seriousness of the Chernobyl accident until some time after it happened. Soviet officials tended to deflect blame from the Kremlin and focus instead on bureaucratic confusion and incompetence at the scene. The officials claimed that the severity of the accident was not made known to Moscow until two days after it happened. One of Gorbachev's advisers was quoted as saying: 'It's true. The news was not well handled at the beginning. Part of that was bungling, but mostly it was due to the difficulty at the top in finding out what had happened and what was going to happen.'[3] The implication was that local officials in the Ukraine failed to alert Moscow either because they believed the accident was not too serious, because they believed it was under control, or because they feared that blame would be pinned on them.

Certainly, there were powerful pressures to play down bad news when reporting to a superior. When he first addressed his countrymen on May 14th about Chernobyl, Gorbachev implicitly put the blame for inaction on local officials. He said: 'As soon as we received reliable initial information, it was made available to the Soviet people and sent through diplomatic channels to the governments of foreign countries.'[4]

The question remains however: *what* did Soviet officialdom know about Chernobyl, and *when* did they know it?

Gorbachev's implicit suggestion that there was a delay before Moscow learned about the seriousness of Chernobyl did not stand up to scrutiny. It was contradicted by other statements and actions. Soviet scientists said privately that the Council of Ministers' office in Moscow was informed of the accident within a few hours. The Council of Ministers reacted quickly by establishing a government commission and dispatching representatives to the scene. The Soviet scientists reported that even though more than one-half of the commission members were in different parts of the Soviet Union, thousands of kilometres apart, they arrived and began work on the same day.[5] Moreover, General Gennadiy Berdov, the deputy minister of internal affairs in the Ukraine, was reported to have reached the Chernobyl power station from Kiev within hours of the explosion.[6]

Ivan Yemelyanov, the deputy director of the agency that

designed the Chernobyl plant, confirmed at a news conference for Western reporters on May 19th that the government commission headed by Soviet Deputy Prime Minister Boris Shcherbina was at work 'on the very day of the accident, April 26th.'[7] Then, in June, the armed forces newspaper, *Red Star*, disclosed that military planning was already under way on April 26th for the helicopter operation to bury the core of the reactor under thousands of tons of sand, lead and other materials.[8]

In a lengthy article extolling the bravery of the helicopter crews, *Red Star* quoted the commander, Major-General Nikolai Antoshchkin, as saying that he received orders to leave urgently for Pripyat on the evening of April 26th. When he arrived the next day, he said, Shcherbina was already on the scene.[9] Other evidence, too, shows that there was information available, early on, that made clear the extent of the Chernobyl disaster.

The Rovno nuclear plant lies 220 miles north-west of Chernobyl, and the Ignalina nuclear plant is located 350 miles to the north in the Soviet Baltic republic of Lithuania. Soviet scientific sources were quoted by one Western reporter as saying that, within hours of the April 26th explosion, the radiation released from Chernobyl activated alarms and automatic shutdown systems at both Rovno and Ignalina.[10] If this happened, it is likely that the duty officers at both plants would have informed Moscow. Even if they didn't, the sudden drop in the generating capacity of the two reactors would likely have caused a disturbance on the national electric power grid, which operates on a thin margin of reserve capacity. The loss of power would have been noticed in Moscow. According to Soviet sources, the KGB maintains officers at all Soviet nuclear facilities, with independent and efficient lines of communication to Moscow.[11] The KGB officers would have had no reason to minimise or cover up the Chernobyl emergency. Indeed, the reverse is true. The job of the KGB is to know what is going on.

One Soviet source was quoted as saying that two days

after the accident, while the Soviet Government was still denying to its European neighbours that anything had happened, the Soviet Politburo met and discussed the accident. At that meeting, the source said, Gorbachev wanted to announce the accident immediately, but a majority of the Politburo decided to say as little as possible at that stage.[12] There was evidence from Poland, too, that Moscow knew almost immediately about the accident. Late on the night of April 26th, unidentified officials in Warsaw were reported to have made discreet inquiries in at least one central hospital and a pharmaceutical supply centre about the availability of potassium iodide solution, the standard remedy against the absorption of radioactive iodine[131].[13] The Polish Government consistently refused to say precisely when or how it learned about the accident. But the Soviets disclosed after the accident that they warned 'one neighbouring country.' Taken together, the evidence is compelling. Western journalists who studied the Soviet response to Chernobyl concluded that the Kremlin must have known almost from the outset that it had a serious problem on its hands.

What about Gorbachev's claim that information was sent through diplomatic channels to foreign governments? Beginning on Monday morning, April 28th, Swedish officials telephoned three Soviet agencies – the Soviet Committee for the Utilisation of Atomic Energy, the Ministry of Electric Power and the State Committee for Safety in the Atomic Power Industry – and asked for information about the high radioactivity readings which were being registered all over Scandinavia. All three agencies said they had no information available. Not until 9 p.m. that night did the Soviet Union issue the first statement about the world's worst nuclear accident. Even then the acknowledgment of the accident – four terse sentences – seemed reluctantly given.

*   *   *

The first Soviet announcement of Chernobyl was followed almost immediately on the Tass news agency wires by a far longer report giving details of the partial meltdown and near-disaster at the Three Mile Island nuclear plant in Pennsylvania in 1979 and of other nuclear accidents in the West. This defensive behaviour derived from a gnawing sense of inferiority that colours Soviet attitudes in dealing with the West, a defensiveness that was crucial in determining the Soviet response to Chernobyl not just in the days after the accident but in the later discussions between Soviet and Western experts at the headquarters of the International Atomic Energy Agency in Vienna and at other fora.

Soviet officials were quick to point out that the West had had its technological failures, too. A second secretary of the Soviet Embassy in Washington, Vitaliy Churkin, answered an invitation in Washington on May Day to testify before a sub-committee of the US House of Representatives, the first such appearance by a Soviet official. Churkin said his appearance symbolised his government's willingness to be 'very forthcoming' about the accident. Displaying a command of English slang and the Gorbachev emphasis on image, he parried questions from representatives for more than an hour. At one stage he was asked to explain in laymen's terms just what had happened at Chernobyl. 'Can you tell me in those same laymen's terms,' he responded, referring to the explosion of the US space shuttle earlier in 1986, 'why the Challenger disaster happened?' The committee chairman, Edward Markey, said: 'Isn't it true, Mr Churkin, in reality, that you should not have been celebrating May Day but radioing Mayday to your citizens and neighbours with regard to the danger?' Churkin parried the criticism. When Markey demanded to know why the Soviet Government had failed to inform its people of the accident, Churkin responded: 'The citizens who were affected by the accident are very well taken care of, and if they have any medical problems, they will not even have medical bills to pay.'

Soviet defensiveness over Chernobyl was also evident during angry exchanges at Wellesley College in Massachusetts. An American specialist on the Soviet economy, Marshall Goldman, was teaching a class which was being attended by two Soviet academics, one of them a professor from Kiev. At one stage the Soviet professor said: 'You have too much information in your country. Sometimes too much information can be a problem.' Goldman exploded in fury: 'When you are risking the life of people and their genetic future by withholding information, that is unconscionable, and despicable.'

Soviet Foreign Ministry press spokesman Vladimir Lomeiko, interviewed in New York soon after the Chernobyl accident had been announced, said that Western reports about the accident were a campaign of disinformation intended to create an image of 'lying Russians.' He added that the water around the Chernobyl plant was 'very good and safe for drinking.'

*   *   *

Traditionally, the Soviet Union had been extremely reluctant to admit mistakes or acknowledge unpleasant truths to its own people. It was difficult for party officials to admit serious failings in a society which claimed to be modelled on the scientific logic of Communism. There was fear that admission of failure in the system could encourage critics to ask awkward questions, even to challenge the legitimacy of party rule.

Above all, the Soviet Union dreaded showing weakness or failings to foreigners because it perceived itself as encircled by a hostile world which would seize on any ammunition, any excuse, to criticise. When he nominated Gorbachev as general secretary in March 1985, Andrei Gromyko, then foreign minister, made a remark which illuminated Soviet insecurities: 'We live in a world in which, figuratively speaking, various telescopes are aimed at the Soviet Union. They watch, just waiting for some sort of crack to appear in the Soviet leadership.'

The Soviet Union's dread of being found wanting or deficient in its dealings with the West is rooted in historical notions of inferiority. The attitude dated from czarist times when Russians were only too aware that theirs was an immensely backward country. The czarist empire covered one-sixth of the land surface of the earth, and yet this empire lagged many years behind Britain or France. At the turn of the twentieth century, three-quarters of its people were peasant farmers or nomadic herdsmen. Two-thirds of its ploughs in 1910 were wooden. Charcoal was still in use in the furnaces of the czar's steelworks. Wood was still used as a fuel to drive railway engines. The backwardness of Russia was a burning source of inferiority to the communist leaders who inherited the czarist empire in October, 1917. Stalin expressed this sense of inferiority in a famous speech in 1931:

> One feature of old Russia was the continual beatings she suffered for falling behind, for her backwardness. She was beaten by the Mongol Khans. She was beaten by the Turkish beys. She was beaten by the Swedish feudal lords. She was beaten by the Polish and Lithuanian gentry. She was beaten by the British and French capitalists. She was beaten by the Japanese barons. All beat her – for her backwardness: for military backwardness, for cultural backwardness, for political backwardness, for industrial backwardness, for agricultural backwardness. She was beaten because to do so was profitable and could be done with impunity . . . we are fifty or a hundred years behind the advanced countries. We must make good this distance in ten years. Either we do it, or they crush us.[15]

The Soviet Union had travelled a long way since the October Revolution of 1917. It had transformed itself into the second most powerful nation on earth. It had put space platforms into orbit and acquired nuclear weapons. It had produced atomic ice breakers, opened up the gas and mineral fields of Siberia and pioneered research in fusion power, lasers and atom smashers. But the nagging insecurities remained. The Soviet Union's reluctance to own up to Chernobyl was partly due to its fear that the unfriendly telescopes of the outside world would focus on Soviet failure.

*   *   *

The silence over Chernobyl was predictable: secrecy in the Soviet Union is both an obsession and a habit of mind. It derives from the fear that knowledge, even of the most rudimentary sort, will be used against the country.

Tourists and foreign residents cannot wander freely in the Soviet Union. Even such basic items as accurate maps are hard to come by, ostensibly because maps could offer assistance to a potential enemy. When tourists collect city plans of Moscow, they discover to their surprise that the plans deliberately have been made incorrect. Much of the country is simply off limits: Gorky, where Andrei Sakharov was exiled, is just one of hundreds of closed cities. Foreigners may travel only on certain highways. And when one travels the road from, say, Moscow to Leningrad, one is aware of the string of observation posts where watchers keep track of comings and goings. In these conditions, it is not surprising that information is among the most precious of commodities. The *New York Times* correspondent David Shipler, who lived in Moscow from 1974 to 1979, described information as 'a choice delicacy.'[16] *Daily Telegraph* Foreign Editor Nigel Wade made much the same point. Wade was the Telegraph's Moscow correspondent before returning to London. Shortly after his return he was visiting a friend who asked about the sources he had developed in Moscow. His response was only half in jest: 'There are no sources in Moscow.' Wade's departure from Moscow pre-dated *glasnost*.

One of the biggest events in recent Soviet history – Khrushchev's 1956 speech to the twentieth Party Congress denouncing Stalin – was startling because it broke the silence within the party about Stalinist terror.[17] But the speech remains unpublished in the Soviet Union. The problem of secrecy is so acute that the Soviet Union is inhibited in talking to itself. On one occasion during the first SALT arms control talks, Soviet military officials privately urged the Americans not to tell their civilian colleagues about Soviet strategic forces.

*   *   *

The concept of news and information in the Soviet Union is different from that in Western countries. Former director general of the Tass news agency N. G. Palgunov put it this way:

> News should not be merely concerned with reporting such and such a fact or event. News or information must pursue a definite goal: it must serve and support the decisions related to the fundamental duties facing our Soviet society, our Soviet people marching on the road of gradual transition from socialism to Communism.[18]

Until the death of Soviet President Leonid Brezhnev in 1982, publication of much information about accidents and natural disasters in the USSR was proscribed by the *Index of Information Not to Be Published in the Open Press*, the guide which tells Soviet journalists what not to report. Until recently, Soviet media routinely ignored or gave only scant coverage to calamities like plane or train crashes, fires, and industrial accidents, or natural disasters like earthquakes. When Ashkabad, the capital of Turkmenia, was flattened by an earthquake in 1948, taking the lives of half the city's population of more than 200,000, only sketchy details were published in the Soviet press after the event. The first real information about what happened was contained in a poem in a literary magazine which was published a few years later. Tashkent, the largest city of Soviet Central Asia, was levelled by an earthquake in 1966. Again, the amount of information that appeared in the Soviet press was limited.

The Soviet media also did not report the 1960 space disaster at the Baikonur launching site in Kazakhstan, which killed several top Soviet military officers including Marshal Mitrofan Nedelin, commander of the Soviet Strategic Rocket Forces. Plane crashes went unreported. They were mentioned only when foreigners were involved, when prominent Soviet citizens were killed or when they occurred in other countries. Even the deaths of Soviet leaders were treated as secret. For the seven months before his death the failure of Yuri Andropov to appear on the public scene was explained simply as a mild illness.

Under Gorbachev, there was a marked change in information policy. The policy of *glasnost* expressly encouraged officials to tell the truth about accidents. The Soviet media reported in unprecedented depth and detail on a number of disasters – including the sinking of the cruise ship, the *Mikhail Lermontov*, off the coast of New Zealand in March, 1986, the *Admiral Nakhimov* in the Black Sea in August, 1986, with the loss of nearly 400 lives and the loss of a Soviet nuclear submarine in October, 1986. Western residents of Moscow said the television coverage of all three accidents was not unlike what would have been seen on British or American television.

Even as late as December, 1986, when a Soviet *Aeroflot* airliner crashed in East Berlin, there was a reluctance to report the tragedy. On the day following the crash, in which seventy people were killed, the newspaper *Pravda* confined its coverage of the crash to announcing that the leadership had sent condolences to the East Germans. The *Pravda* report did not indicate that the airliner was Soviet.

*   *   *

In 1839, the French traveller Astolphe Louis Leonard said of the Russia he encountered:

> Secrecy presides over everything, administrative secrecy, political, social secrecy . . . Here everything is difficult. Everybody wishes to please his master by contributing towards the concealment of some corner of the truth from foreigners . . . everyone here, you see, thinks about what no one says.[19]

Imperial Russia, like the modern Soviet Union, operated on a need-to-know basis. This was hardly surprising. An autocratic system in which the czar was the representative of God on earth was not likely to foster consultation. Article 1 of the Fundamental Laws of 1892 decreed that:

> The all-Russian Emperor is an autocrat and unlimited monarch – God himself commands his supreme power be obeyed out of conscience as well as fear.[20]

There was little about the pre-revolutionary system in Russia that resembled what modern Westerners think of as the monarchy. The czar was not a smiling symbol of the state who rode around the countryside opening factories, going on walk-abouts and chatting encouragingly with the local populace. He was at the pinnacle of a system of control and administration which relied not on consent but enforced obedience to maintain itself in power. The czar ruled through a vast and secretive bureaucracy. There was nothing in the imperial system that required him to explain or justify himself. He had, until the new constitution of 1905, no political parties to deal with, for they were considered to represent particular interests and were therefore incompatible with czarist rule.

After 1905, there were signs of real change in Russia – the czar accepted his constitutional status and there were beginnings of Western-style democracy. But powerful forces inside the country worked against change and the tragedy of the First World War effectively brought the movement for reform to a halt. Even had the war not intervened, it is unclear whether the reforms could have succeeded. The notion of autocracy was one of the bases upon which the entire czarist system was established. Historically, that notion of czarist autocracy was bolstered by the Orthodox Church.

The Orthodox Church is itself fond of secrecy – the faithful are not permitted to witness the consecration of the host at Orthodox Mass. Instead that is done at the high altar which is shielded from view by a screen, and the worshippers come forward only as far as the screen to make their communion.

In order to maintain the autocratic system, it was necessary for the czar to have a means of coercion and control. Ivan IV had a personal force of armed men called the *oprichniki* which he used to institute a reign of terror that cemented his position as absolute ruler. By the end of the seventeenth century, Peter the Great had established the first secret police department in the country, the Transfiguration Office. In one of its first operations, Peter's secret police were employed to put down an attempted military revolt, which they did by torturing 1,200 men by flogging, roasting and breaking on the wheel.

After the attempted Decembrist military plot of 1825, Czar Nicholas ordered that no mention of the attempted mutiny should appear in the press. More to the point, he established in the Third Section of his personal chancellery an internal security organisation designed to keep track of all subversive ideas and organisations. The Third Section had secret informers, and it acted as a judicial body with power to punish or send into exile those who were found to be a danger to the state.

The czarist state, until the 1917 October Revolution, saw a continuing struggle between autocracy and the forces of change in Russia, with an ever-tightening grip on the spread of ideas and the growth of subversive organisations. There is nothing surprising in the fact that after the revolution, the new Soviet Union grew quickly to resemble the old czarist regime in so many ways. The emphasis on secrecy, the insistence on the absolute right of the Communist Party to rule, the secret police establishment – all owe much to the czarist origins of the contemporary Soviet state.

*   *   *

It was Lenin who insisted that the nascent Communist Party in pre-revolutionary Russia be organised on a secretive, need-to-know basis. This was a direct result of the party's illegality, itself a reflection of its avowedly revolutionary aims. In his book *What Is To be Done?*, Lenin wrote:

> Only an incorrigible utopian would have a broad organisation of workers with elections, reports, universal suffrage, etc., under the autocracy.[21]

Lenin proposed a tightly-controlled, centralised party of professional revolutionaries, operating under strict discipline in a cellular structure that could not be easily infiltrated or destroyed by agents of the imperial state. This structure, adopted by the Bolshevik faction of the Russian Social Democratic Workers Party, was their strength when facing a hostile environment. Lenin argued that:

> The only serious organisational principle for the active workers of our movement should be the strictest secrecy, the strictest selection of members, and the training of professional revolutionaries. Given these qualities, something even more than 'democratism' would be guaranteed to us, namely complete, comradely, mutual confidence among revolutionaries.[22]

As a revolutionary organiser, Lenin proved his genius. Despite the fact that in the only democratic election ever held in Russia or the Soviet Union – the election of the Constituent Assembly after the October Revolution – Lenin's party won only a quarter of the votes, the Bolsheviks ended up in charge of the revolutionary state. Secrecy and conspiracy had triumphed.

On Lenin's death in 1924, Stalin seized control of the party. Under Stalin, who ruled the Soviet Union until his death in 1953, totalitarianism was carried to its furthest limits. Terror and oppression were the hallmarks of Stalinist society. It was an era when every Soviet citizen went in dread of a ubiquitous and fearsome security police. In the worst years of Stalin's terror, everyone feared being woken in the early hours of the morning by a knock on the door, dragged out of bed and snatched away from their families, usually forever. The terror reinforced traditional habits of caution and circumspection.

Under Stalin, truth was obliterated by propaganda. Even the great dictator himself could not trust the news that his own news agencies produced. During the Second World War, while Soviet press reports spoke of victories that never were and hid from the Soviet people the true course of the war, Stalin listened to the Russian-language broadcasts of foreign radio stations. It was in that way that he learned of the execution by the Germans of his son, Yakov. Stalin's successors, Nikita Khrushchev, Leonid Brezhnev and Yuri Andropov were all said to have been avid listeners to foreign broadcasts. Brezhnev was said to be particularly interested in the *Voice of America*'s analysis of Soviet politics. Andropov was said to be interested in the undistorted news broadcasts by the *BBC*[23].

* * *

The explosion of the No. 4 reactor unit of the Chernobyl Atomic Power Plant in the early morning hours of April 26th, 1986, was on one level nothing more than a massive industrial accident. Valery Legasov, the first deputy director of the I. V. Kurchatov Atomic Energy Institute and a leader of the investigation into the accident, called Chernobyl one of several industrial accidents in recent years that had caused massive damage and human losses. He was right. It would be hard not to draw comparisons between Chernobyl and the 1985 Bhopal disaster in India which left more than 2,000 people dead and perhaps 200,000 more human beings facing threats to their health. Or there was the explosion of a gas storage unit in central Mexico City, which sent a fireball across a heavily-populated slum area.

On that level Chernobyl was a major human tragedy. Thirty-one people were reported dead from the effects of radiation sickness or other causes. Hundreds more received such high doses of radiation that their long-term health prospects are grim. The fallout from the plant, which spread across the European Soviet Union and much of Western and Eastern Europe, means that thousands will die premature deaths from radiation-induced cancers. A region around the plant bigger than Luxembourg was officially declared too contaminated for human habitation, and it is clear that a much wider area of the Ukraine and Byelorussia suffered serious contamination from radioactive fallout. At least 135,000 people fled their homes. As far away as Great Britain, radioactive fallout contaminated sheep farms in England, Scotland and Wales. The reckoning from Chernobyl will be high.

As an industrial accident, Chernobyl appears likely to be the most costly in history. It deserved attention for that reason alone. However, it was important to recognise that Chernobyl happened at a specific time and for specific reasons. In West Germany, in the days after the accident, a new slogan was born: 'Chernobyl is everywhere.' These ambiguous words, like most slogans, were only half-right. Chernobyl was an example of the dangers of the modern industrial world. But Chernobyl happened not in Sweden or in Italy but in a small town in the Ukraine. The accident has profound international implications but the story of Chernobyl is also a story of the Soviet Union.

3

STALIN'S LEGACY

We are not muddling through, comrades.

Mikhail Gorbachev[1]

The Chernobyl disaster happened at a time of crisis in the Soviet Union. Basic elements of Soviet political organisation were facing unprecedented public scrutiny, while at the same time the economy was being subjected to some of the harshest strains it had faced since the days after the Second World War. It was the fate of the new man at the head of the country, Mikhail Gorbachev, to have to address all these problems at once.

Gorbachev came to power with the knowledge that his tenure of office depended on how well he dealt with the myriad problems that had developed over the complacent Brezhnev era, problems that Yuri Andropov had only started to tackle before his death and that had been set aside by Konstantin Chernenko. Gorbachev had tackled the difficulties head on.

Alcohol abuse was a growing problem in the Soviet Union, both a cause and an expression of social and economic ills. Gorbachev pushed through higher prices for spirits, limited sales hours at liquor stores and ordered cutbacks in drinking at official functions. Workers were failing to meet productivity targets. Gorbachev mounted a drive for labour discipline that included sweeps through cinemas by militiamen looking for workers who were playing truant from their jobs. Furthermore, too many workers were ignoring their official jobs in order to concentrate on more lucrative black market activities. Gorbachev ordered a crackdown on illegal incomes, including provisions that would require explanation of the source of large deposits in the banks.

These actions caught the headlines. But they were, in fact, a sideshow. The real problem was a fundamental crisis in the way the Soviet Union was managed. Across the board, old assumptions about how socialist production should be managed were under sceptical scrutiny. The accident at Chernobyl, afflicting as it did one of the commanding heights of Soviet technology, would inevitably heighten that scrutiny.

Although it may seem like a digression, in order to understand what the Chernobyl disaster meant to the Soviet Union, it is essential to understand something of the situation in which the world's second superpower found itself on April 26th, 1986.

*   *   *

One of the ironies of history is that Marxism, which was based in great measure on observations of Victorian industrial England, found its firmest roots in Russia. Karl Marx wrote about the problems of industrial capitalism. But Russia was hardly a capitalist state. It was, before the revolution, the least industrialised of the major European countries. Its working class – traditionally, the manual labourers who toil in factories – was minuscule. In 1913, only nine per cent of the Russian labour force was employed in manufacturing and construction. As late as 1928, eleven years after the revolution, only 17.6 per cent of the population could be considered to be part of the Marxist working class. Instead, pre-revolutionary Russia was largely a peasant state. In 1913, seventy-five per cent of the people of Russia worked on the land. As late as 1926, only seventeen per cent of the Soviet people lived in cities and towns.

The fact that Russia did not have a big urban proletariat

caused considerable problems for the Russian Marxists.
They carried on a great debate over whether a Communist
revolution was possible in Russia because Marx had postu-
lated Communism as developing out of fully-fledged capitalism, not from a near-feudal, agrarian autocracy. One of
Lenin's early achievements was to devise a formulation
which adapted Marxist thought on this subject to the
Russian situation. Lenin argued that all of Russia could be
considered an 'international proletariat,' exploited by the
other European powers in just the same way that capitalists
exploited individual members of the working class.

The stated goal of the Russian Revolution was to seize
for the people who worked in the factories – the working
class – the control of the state. But if the working class was
now in control, it exercised this control only through its
vanguard, the professional revolutionaries (who were
themselves not necessarily members of the working class).
Lenin put it this way:

> The rule of the working class is reflected in the con-
> stitution, the ownership and the fact that it is we who are
> running things, while management is quite another mat-
> ter: it is a question of skill, a question of experience. . . .
> In order to manage, one must know the job and be a
> splendid administrator. . . . Administrative experience
> does not fall from heaven and is not a gift of the Holy
> Spirit. And that is why the most progressive class is not
> automatically that which is capable of administer-
> ing. . . . For the administration and construction of the
> state, we need people who are masters of administrative
> technique, who have political and economic experience.[3]

These 'masters of administrative technique' would move
into power and use their skills to set up the Marxist
'dictatorship of the proletariat' in the Soviet Union on
behalf of the 'most progressive class,' the tiny Russian
urban proletariat.

*   *   *

Today in the Soviet Union, there are more than a hundred separate government ministries, charged with everything from supervising the paper industry to the production of steam turbines. But that is only one layer of administration. For in addition to the ranks of government administrators, the Communist Party bureaucracy has a role – often the dominant role – to play in the running of the Soviet Union. The role of the party in relation to the state was defined by Lenin when he said that 'No single decision is taken by a single state organ in our republic without the guiding instructions of the party Central Committee.'[4]

In the Central Committee of the party, an administrative apparatus is installed to supervise the work of the government ministries. And these structures of supervision are replicated all the way down to the level of local administration, where local party officials have a role to play in supervising the administration of factories and other producers. The party is deeply involved in the management of the economy. As a contemporary Soviet writer on management systems, Gavrill Popov, says:

Party control holds a special place and in a socialist society goes down to the core of activities of all state and social organisations.[5]

Not only does the party supervise the decisions taken by the managers of industry – it is actively involved in their selection. According to Popov:

The leading role in personnel management belongs to the party organisations, organs of party leadership and also the superior bodies of economic management. The party organs perform not only directive but also operational functions: they create management reserves, assess the personnel, issue their recommendations to the economic management bodies concerning candidates for promotion, shifting of workers, etc.

This role of the party organs stems from the principle

that selection of personnel is the duty of the owner of the means of production. . . . The party is the leader of society and in its capacity of the vanguard of society it directs the key functions of management – the selection of personnel and the formation of the system of management. . . .

There is a name for this system of personnel selection – the nomenclature, or, in Russian, the *nomenklatura*. Popov mentions the *nomenklatura* briefly. He says:

The nomenclature is an important element in the staffing system and it exists in two basic forms. The first provides a list of posts within the given body which can be substituted or relieved by a higher body (under an agreement with party organs). The second nomenclature lists the posts which the given management body can deal with at its own discretion, although the candidates for appointment are to be approved by one or another organ of party leadership. The nomenclature realises the principle of centralised management of the national economy, the principle of the leading role of the party.

Simply put, the party selects those who direct the affairs of the state and the economy.

The *nomenklatura* does not embrace only the top rank of jobs in the Soviet Union. Consider for instance the city of Novosibirsk, a Siberian city of about 1.4 million people. In 1971, some information about the city committee's *nomenklatura* lists was published in Moscow. Here is how the system was described:

The party committee itself decides which posts to include in the *nomenklatura*. For instance, nearly 800 posts are on the *nomenklatura* of Novosibirsk town committee. Included on it are the secretaries and heads of departments of the committees at the next level down of the party; chairpersons and deputy chairpersons of the executive committees of the Soviets [councils]; the directors, chief engineers and secretaries of party committees of large industrial enterprises and building sites; the heads of higher educational institutions; and other employees with a high level of responsibility.[6]

A former member of the *nomenklatura*, Michael Voslensky, estimates the total strength of the *nomenklatura* in the Soviet Union at about 750,000 people.[7] These three-quarters of a million people are the managers and the rulers of the Soviet Union today. Entry into the *nomenklatura* is the passport into a privileged élite sector of special stores, special services, foreign travel and power. The *nomenklatura* has become a ruling class in the Soviet Union, a class that has acquired wealth from power, the mirror image of the capitalist exploiter who acquires power from wealth. As the Soviet economy has grown, more and more managers have been required, building up both the size and strength of the *nomenklatura*.

The problem facing the Soviet Union in the field of management is that despite this ever-growing number of party-vetted *nomenklatura* administrators and managers, the Soviet Union has yet to manage the feat of producing an efficient, post-industrial economy.

*   *   *

The Soviet Union has celebrated heavy industry since the early days after the Revolution. It shows pride in machines and engineering might. It lauds the feats of builders, power workers, oil-drillers. It has put science and technology on a pedestal. It exhibits its gigantic industrial projects – dams, steelworks, tractor factories, power plants – to the world as an example of what the Communist system can achieve.

The media give a high priority to industrial stories. Output figures for coal, steel and electricity production are cited on the evening television news programme, *Vremya*. Newsreels show lines of combine harvesters advancing in echelons through fields of rippling grain. Newspapers feature interviews with factory workers who have over-fulfilled their production quotas. Radio Moscow's English-language service boasts about record cement and truck production.

Soviet officials take an almost Victorian pride in some of the great industrial achievements of the Soviet state: the construction of the giant Kama River truck factory, the Bratsk hydro-electric station, the Baikal-Amur railroad. Soviet officials from local party secretaries to senior Polit-buro members reel off production figures with the same kind of infatuation with output as was shown by industrial-ists in nineteenth century Manchester. Above all, there is belief in the inexorable march of industrial progress. The temples of the modern state are the dams, hydroelectric stations, steel mills, chemical plants, coal mines, truck factories, scientific laboratories and nuclear power plants that have been built across the Soviet Union since 1917.

The Soviet industrial, scientific and technological record is a mixed one, with major achievements in some areas being balanced by dismal failures in others. The Soviet Union put the first artificial satellite into space, it sent the first man, Yuri Gagarin, into orbit and it has sent spacecraft to the planets. The Soviet Union developed the world's largest network of hydroelectric stations, opened up the gas and mineral fields of Siberia, produced atomic ice breakers and optical telescopes, built railways in some of the most inhospitable terrain on earth and has developed gigantic steel, mining and engineering industries. The Soviet Union pioneered research in, among other things, fusion power, lasers and atom smashers. It long ago surpassed the United States in output of steel, cement and oil. In general, if the state puts sufficient priority on a project, the chances are that the Soviet system will do the job, and often do it quite well. The requirements of the military, for instance, are given the highest priority.

In other ways, Soviet industrial society has failed spec-tacularly. It is immensely inefficient. A high percentage of goods produced by Soviet factories is defective or so shoddily made they are fit only for the scrap heap. The Soviet Union has shown itself unable to master the problem of quality control. The Soviet press often highlights absurd cases of industrial inefficiency: 13,000 pairs of sun glasses produced by a factory in the Ukraine with lenses too dark to see through; over half the milk sold in cardboard cartons in Moscow spoiled because defective packaging machinery tore a hole in the cartons; children's plastic balls that burst like soap bubbles when kicked.[8] The Soviet Union can put satellites in space, but it cannot make a reliable washing machine. It can carry out sophisticated viral research, but it cannot keep elevators working. It can build nuclear missiles, but it cannot keep factory production lines running. Soviet industry is plagued by shortages of materials and spare parts because of breakdowns and bottlenecks in the supply system. Soviet industry squanders resources and energy. The system is characterised by waste, bureaucratic rigidity and uneven development. Soviet industry is over-staffed. Soviet planners have a fondness for grandiose projects and enormous construction schemes which often produce unexpected environmental problems. Soviet industrialisation has been carried out without regard for the need to protect nature.

The Soviet system of central planning produces amusing examples of waste and inefficiency: freight trains from Moscow taking concrete roof beams to Leningrad, passing on the way trains from Leningrad carrying concrete beams to Moscow; empty trains running around the country-side to run up the monthly mileage required by the Plan; water trucks hosing down city streets in the middle of thunderstorms.[9]

What about technology? Soviet industry is notoriously poor at producing good modern technology, and bureaucratic inertia does not encourage a climate of innovation. The classic example is the Soviet failure in the field of computer technology and microelectronics. According to one estimate, the Soviet Union is as much as a decade behind the West in computer technology. Eric Firdman, former deputy chief designer at a Leningrad design bureau, now living in Boston, said the major research computer in the Soviet Union today is a reproduction of a British computer made in 1959. The most widely-used business computer in the Soviet Union is a copy of the IBM 360, which became obsolete in the United States a decade ago.[10]

When the Ministry of the Electronics Industry promised General Secretary Leonid Brezhnev that it would produce the first Soviet-made electronic calculator in time for the twenty-fourth Party Congress in 1971, it promised more than it could deliver. Soviet engineers could not figure out how to make the assembly onto which the integrated circuits would be welded. Eventually, the engineers, by now desperate, dismantled a Japanese calculator and stamped the American-made microchips with a Soviet trade mark. A second Japanese-made calculator was taken apart and its interior parts put into a Soviet-made container. The calculator was presented to Brezhnev on schedule, but it was not until two years later that the Soviets were able to mass-produce calculators. (They cost eight times more than Japanese calculators.)

The Soviet Union has always relied heavily on imported foreign technology. For years a routine practice has been to buy Western technology, and then reverse-engineer it. The Soviet Union expends time, money and effort trying to obtain Western technology which is on the Western list of goods which are not permitted to be exported to the Soviet Union because they might have a military application. The Pentagon estimates that the Soviet Union earmarks roughly one billion dollars a year for buying Western hardware and documents.

Soviet science is also problematic. In the years after the Second World War, after the Soviets acquired nuclear weapons, the United States was worried by accounts of the brilliance of Soviet scientists and mathematicians. The myth grew up of a society of young geniuses, idling in cafés in Leningrad or Moscow and casually doodling brilliant mathematical formulae on the backs of envelopes. It is true that the Soviet Union has produced brilliant mathematicians and scientists. But much Soviet applied science is second-rate.

The Soviet Union has one-quarter of the world's scientists, and half of the world's engineers work in the Soviet Union. The Soviet Union invests more than three per cent of its gross national product in research and development. It has created an unmatched system of scientific education in schools. The Soviet Union produces more college-educated graduates in science and technology than any other country. It produces more than twice as many science and technology graduates (450,000 in 1983) as the United States (200,000). Yet with what result? Russian or Soviet citizens have won only ten of the 370 science prizes since the Nobel Prize was first awarded in 1901. The Americans have won 137. In the past ten years, only one Nobel science prize has gone to a Soviet. He was physicist Peter Kapitza, who spent thirteen years as a researcher at Cambridge University.[11]

*   *   *

To understand why Soviet industrial society developed as it did, it is necessary to look back to Josef Stalin, who succeeded as Soviet leader after the death of Lenin in 1924.

Stalin was an unlikely heir to Lenin. Where the majority of the Communist leadership was part of the intelligentsia, Stalin was the product of a truly reactionary educational institution – an Orthodox theological seminary. His parents were peasants. His rise to power was through the back door of the party. While the intellectuals of the movement were living in exile, Stalin was back in Russia, supervising the party press in Baku and doing the unglamorous and dangerous work of carrying out the intellectuals' decisions. It was not until 1912 that Stalin left Russia and then only for a short stay in Vienna where he was sent by Lenin to study how the Russian Communists should treat the various nationalities in the empire. When he returned to Russia the following year, he was arrested by the czarist secret police and sent into internal exile in Siberia, where he remained until the 1917 Revolution.

In 1922, he became general secretary of the party. This was, at the time, a new post, and subservient to the Politburo and the Central Executive Committee. In his post, Stalin supervised the work of cadre selection, a task which earned him the nickname of 'Comrade Card-Index.' It was a joke that turned sour for many of the potential rivals for power who repeated it, for it was through his control over the cadres – the *nomenklatura* – that Stalin was to work out what became the second revolution, a redirection of the Soviet society and economy so profound that Stalin's successors are still grappling with it today.

Stalin's first Five-Year Plan, beginning in October 1928, laid the foundations of an advanced industrial society by giving priority to heavy industry, fuel, power and communications. The needs of Soviet consumers came bottom on his list. Stalin set out to telescope into a few decades the industrialisation process which had evolved over several centuries in Western Europe and the United States. 'The whole of Russia was hurled into a gigantic struggle to build socialism, to transform Russia from a backward agricultural country into an advanced socialist nation.'[13] This Plan did not meet its targets (many were wildly ambitious) but it was spectacularly successful in increasing industrial production. In the space of a few years, Stalin had succeeded in creating a mighty engineering industry. 'Russia, the country where two-thirds of all ploughs had been wooden until 1910, now boasted industries producing machine-tools, turbines, tractors and metallurgical equipment and produced more electricity than it could use.'[14] A slogan of the 1920s and 1930s expressed the achievement felt by the Communist leaders: 'There are no fortresses that Bolsheviks cannot storm.'

The emphasis Stalin placed on heavy industry, his rejection of balanced planning, his relentless emphasis on

output, the low priority given to consumer needs and his
determination to modernise the Soviet Union at a breakneck pace, regardless of human cost, left an indelible mark
on the Soviet Union. Stalin was responsible for the unique
way in which Soviet industrial society has developed.
Moreover, the Soviet industrialisation programme was
achieved at immense human cost. The industrial scene
became like a battlefield, with workers and materials being
rushed to new 'fronts' or new 'campaigns.' Industrial
'breakthroughs' were reported in Soviet newspapers like
military victories. Factories were in fierce competition with
each other to secure scarce resources or skilled labour.
Party officials had to use their influence to get hold of
materials and supplies.

The story of how Stalin's Soviet Union became an industrial power is one of human degradation, malnutrition,
starvation and death. Even today, no one knows for sure
how many people died or lost their liberty in Stalin's quest
for industrialisation and the purges and terror that accompanied it. But in 1956, Nikita Khrushchev said that of 1,966
delegates to the 1934 party congress, 1,108 had been
arrested in purges. And about seventy per cent of the 1934
Central Committee members and candidate members were
shot during Stalinist purges. Millions more ordinary Soviet
citizens were forced into what can only be called slave
labour camps. Some say the number was in the low millions
while others place the figure at nearer twenty million. In the
Ukraine, there was a famine that led to untold deaths. And
a census of Kazakhstan in 1937 showed so many fewer
Kazakhs than would have been expected that the census
was suppressed.

*   *   *

Stalin established the tyranny of the economic plan
at the centre of Soviet life. Meeting planning targets became the fundamental law of the land. Under Stalin,
industrial managers and party officials were rewarded with

prestige and privileges if they met the targets. If they failed, they faced dismissal, disgrace, even arrest on charges of sabotage. But planning targets were usually set ambitiously high and it was not enough to meet them. 'Overfulfil the plan' became the battle cry of the industrialising Soviet state.

This emphasis on meeting unrealistic planning targets bred some curious industrial practices which are still present today in the Soviet Union. The relentless emphasis on output means that industrial managers tend to neglect quality in the scramble to meet their targets. They are rewarded for how much they produce, not for the excellence of their products. In practice, this means that many of the industrial items or consumer goods leaving Soviet factories are defective, or junk fit only for a scrap yard. From Stalin's time on, Soviet industry has been plagued by bottlenecks in the supply of raw materials and components. Central planning has proved unable to devise an efficient supply system. On many days, factories are unable to work at full capacity. Soviet industrial managers employ *tolkachi* or pushers – semi-illegal middlemen – to bribe or pressurise suppliers to send materials on time. But often, when supplies finally show up, there are only a few days left to fulfil the monthly, quarterly or annual plan.

Soviet managers solve this problem by resorting to a practice which began during Stalin's era called 'Storming the Plan'. The practice, *shturmovshchina*, refers to the national phenomenon of crash programmes which require factories and workers to labour round the clock in a frantic, last-ditch bid to meet their output targets. It produces wildly erratic work rhythms in factories, large and small. Workers often sit around doing nothing for most of the month and then have to labour extremely hard for a few days. Another stratagem employed by industrial managers is 'featherbedding.' Factories keep many more workers on their payrolls than they actually need to cope with unexpected problems or breakdowns. This practice contributes to a labour shortage in many parts of the Soviet Union.

Moreover, managers tend to hoard tools, raw materials and equipment in case of sudden emergencies. Perishable materials are left to rot in factory yards, and expensive equipment is left to rust in the rain. But managers regard any means as justified in meeting the demands of the plan.

If managers cannot meet their targets, they routinely engage in deception. The practice of fudging output figures is so widespread that many citizens disbelieve official claims about plan fulfilment. In a pamphlet entitled *Free Thought*, which circulated in the early 1970s, an economist with the pseudonym A. Babushkin made a comparison of published statistics with reality. His study showed that from 1966 to 1970, only twenty-six per cent of the planned number of cars, forty per cent of tractors, seventy per cent of electrical power, seventy-one per cent of steel and fifty-eight per cent of canned goods had been produced, in spite of party claims in 1971 that all major indices of the Five-Year Plan had been fulfilled.[15]

Propaganda aimed at encouraging workers to increase output and raise productivity was a key element of Stalin's five-year plans. The feats of individual workers were glorified. The hero of the campaign for 'overfulfilment' in the Stalin years was Alexei Stakhanov, a coal miner in the Donbass, who was said to have hewed 102 tons of coal in a single shift instead of the seven tons demanded. The exercise was an unreal one. The feat was achieved only by halting all other work in his sector of the mine and by using a gang of miners to help him. But the opportunity was used to raise work norms. Workers who emulated Stakhanov were called Stakhanovites, and they were given the best housing and pay rises. Some Stakhanovite workers were lynched by their fellow-workers.

Today, the party attempts to use honour and praise to motivate workers and tries to link the concept of hard work with patriotism and good citizenship. Every Soviet factory has a display board showing photographs of Soviet workers who have over-fulfilled their production quotas, or performed outstanding work. Wage rises are a limited incentive since there is too much money in circulation and not enough to spend it on.[16]

*　　*　　*

Gigantomania was another legacy of the Stalin years. A fondness for 'gigantism' in the construction of dams, hydro-electric schemes and factories was a mark of Stalinist development. The Dnieper Dam, started in 1927, was destined to be the largest hydroelectric station in the world. The second largest steelworks in the world arose at the 'Iron Mountain' in Magnitogorsk in the Urals during the first Five-Year Plan. These huge new construction pro-grammes, which were aimed at transforming the Soviet economy in one great leap forward, also answered a psychological need: they were a demonstration of what Communist man could achieve.

Stalin was the main initiator of gigantism: he was ob-sessed with rerouting Russia's great rivers, building chains of dams and constructing massive hydroelectric schemes. The showpiece of his programme was the refashioning of the Volga River, which is the longest Soviet river west of the Urals. In the 1930s, work began on thirteen large dams on the Volga. Canals were dug and river channels enlarged. By 1937, Stalin had linked Moscow to the Volga and the Caspian Sea, as well as to the White and Baltic seas. The scheme was a triumph of gigantism, and it paved the way for many other land improvement schemes. (Only later did Soviet scientists recognise the environmental damage.)

Marshall Goldman has called Stalin: 'the greatest re-arranger of nature the world has ever seen. . . .'[17] Other rulers had had the dictatorial power to give orders and divert manpower and equipment, but until Stalin no one had the technology as well as the power to carry out such huge undertakings over such a vast expanse. Whether such schemes were economically warranted seemed immaterial to Stalin.

The modern Soviet Union still exhibits gigantomania.

The most dramatic modern example was the construction of the Kama River truck plant in the 1970s. The world's largest truck plant, located about 600 miles east of Moscow, occupies twenty-three square miles, an area larger than the entire island of Manhattan. It is far larger than anything in Detroit or the Ruhr. Costing many millions of roubles, it comprises mile upon mile of pipelines, computer-run conveyor belts and assembly lines. Each year it turns out tens of thousands of heavy trucks and diesel engines.

*   *   *

Stalinist economics was based on the unswerving quest for growth – the central goal of Stalin's economic programme was to make the Soviet Union into an industrial state, with railroads, steel mills, engineering works and all the other industrial enterprises that made up the infrastructure of developed economies of the day. But Stalin could not use capitalist methods to achieve those goals. To do so would have meant abandoning the monopoly on decision-making that was central to the party's control of the country. Instead, Stalin reapplied the methods of the czars with a vengeance. Stalin dragged the Soviet Union into the modern industrial world through the method of centralised control of industry and through the use of compulsion on the work force.

The Second World War brought the industrialisation drive to a grinding halt, and the Soviet Union faced military punishment worse than any of the other allied powers. The German invasion of 1941 cut Soviet industrial output in half and took more than a third of the Soviet population under the control of the occupying army. By the end of the war, the Soviet Union was a devastated victor with twenty million dead from the war and an economy that was largely in ruins. For Stalin, the end of the war meant a return to the push for industrialisation. He said that when the Soviet Union could produce fifty million tons of pig iron, sixty million tons of steel, sixty million tons of oil and 500 million tons of coal each year, then the country 'could be guaranteed against all possible accidents.' By 1950, the Soviet Union ranked as the world's second industrial power. Shortly after Stalin's death in 1953, all of the dictator's production goals were achieved.

That achievement was not the end of the race, though. It was only a milestone.

* * *

As recently as the mid 1950s, the Soviet Union seemed on the verge of a major economic takeoff. In 1957, the launch of the world's first artificial satellite, the Sputnik, appeared to be the first sign of a new era. The Soviet leader Nikita Khrushchev, in a boastful and buoyant mood, warned the West: 'We will bury you.' He wasn't threatening to kill off the capitalist world, simply to watch it die as the superior Soviet system overcame it. It was precisely at this moment that the signs of strain in the economy appeared. In 1958, the rate of growth of the Soviet economy began to decline. Falling rates of growth have been a feature of the Soviet economy ever since.

According to figures compiled by the American Central Intelligence Agency, the rate of growth in the Soviet economy dropped from 11.1 per cent in 1958 to 3.7 per cent in 1978. Soviet figures show a slightly lower rate for 1958, slightly higher for 1978, but the trend is clear: dramatic fall-off in the expansion of the economy.

The meteoric rise of the Soviet economy until 1958 (though interrupted by the Second World War), accompanied though much of it was by terror and brutality, seemed to offer some sort of legitimation of the Marxist-Leninist-Stalinist model as a way to create a modern industrial state. But the persistent economic difficulties that have characterised the Soviet Union since the late 1950s have delegitimised the Soviet experience for many, including many Western Marxists and former supporters of the Soviet system.

   At the root of the contemporary challenge to the Soviet
economy was the need to convert from a system of *extensive*
growth to one of *intensive* growth. In layman's terms, what
this means is getting growth through a greater return on
investment rather than by investing more.

   Intensive growth became a hot issue in the Soviet Union
when the chief of the KGB, Yuri Andropov, became
general secretary of the party in 1983 after the death of
Leonid Brezhnev. Andropov, and the men around him,
like Mikhail Gorbachev, had come to realise that the Soviet
Union could not hope to keep its economy growing by
simply putting in more labour, more oil, more grain and
more steel. The Soviet Union, like other developing countries before it, had run up against the problem of making a
transition from rapid industrialisation to management of a
developed economy.

   In fact, the Soviet Union had hit that problem many
years earlier. But rather than deal with it, the tired leaders
around Leonid Brezhnev had allowed the country to drift.
By the time Brezhnev died, there was general agreement
that a drastic change of direction was needed. Andropov
came to power with plans to revitalise the economy by
improving labour discipline. No one can say how far he
might have got with that effort had he not become ill almost
as soon as he took office. His death in 1984 was followed by
a thirteen-month standstill when old guard Konstantin
Chernenko served as general secretary. When Chernenko
died, the party turned to an Andropov protegé, Gorbachev, hoping that he would be able to find a way to deal
with the intractable problem of revitalising the Soviet
economy without disrupting the party's power. By the
mid-1980s, even within the top ranks of the country's
political élite, there was serious concern about the failings
of the economic system. For Mikhail Gorbachev and the
men around him, the pressure was on, long before
Chernobyl, to do something dramatic about the economic
crisis facing the Soviet Union.

                    *   *   *

Early in September 1985, Mikhail Gorbachev set off on the most important domestic trip of his young administration. As is the custom when the top Soviet leader leaves Moscow, he was seen off at the airport by a big delegation of senior party and government officials, including Andrei Gromyko, Nikolai Ryzhkov and Eduard Shevardnadze. Gorbachev's plane landed in the western Siberian city of Nizhnevartovsk, home of 178,000 people, many of them employed in the servicing of the vast Samotlor oil and gas field of the *oblast*, or province, of Tyumen. The city is a raw place, built up rapidly over the past two decades. Even today, there is no cinema in the city, and living conditions are tough. Every year, new people come to Nizhnevartovsk, looking for a chance to make money or make new lives. But every year, many people move out because they cannot stand up to the demands of Siberia.

Gorbachev went to Nizhnevartovsk to deal with a major threat to the economic health of the Soviet Union – a production crisis in the country's most important oil and gas fields. He was going to Tyumen Province both to encourage the workers and to give them some blunt talk. Soviet television covered the trip extensively, including his visits to gas plants, power stations and supply bases for the oil fields.

In the city of Surgut, Gorbachev toured an exhibit organised by the local enterprise, Surgutneftegas. His guide was Oil Industry Minister Dinkov. The exhibit was not a boastful one. Instead, Gorbachev was shown defective metal parts produced by a works in Baku, equipment from a factory in Kharkov that came without proper controls, substandard cable sleeves from a factory in Tashkent and other shoddy goods. The message that Dinkov and the arrangers of the exhibit hoped to get across to Gorbachev was that they were having trouble doing their jobs because they didn't get the materials they needed. On the following day, Gorbachev, accompanied by Boris Yeltsin, Boris Shcherbina and party Central Committee Secretary Dolgikh, sat down with a group of party and

industry officials for some frank talk about the problems in
the West Siberian oil fields. It was a strong performance
by Gorbachev.[19]

He praised the productivity of Tyumen, which was providing sixty per cent of the total Soviet oil output and
fifty-five per cent of its gas. It was, he said, 'an outstanding
achievement, an unprecedented one in world practice.'
Then, Gorbachev's mood shifted. He chuckled and said:

> Perhaps it is also worth congratulating you on this,
> because the positive part will end soon and I shall get
> down to shortcomings, and shortcomings are not
> something abstract. These shortcomings have their
> perpetrators.

The audience chuckled with Gorbachev at this remark, but
there was an undercurrent of nervousness. They knew what
was coming. Gorbachev was blunt:

> The CPSU Central Committee is worried about the fact
> that for the third year the Tyumen region is not fulfilling
> plans for the extraction of oil.

Gorbachev complained that while many people in the
industry were working well, many others had a 'here today,
gone tomorrow' outlook which tolerated shoddy, flimsy
equipment and poor construction. He said he was embarrassed that there was no place for the residents of
Nizhnevartovsk to watch a movie. He said that he had
reprimanded *oblast* party and government officials for
failing to pay enough attention to living conditions of
workers. It was a classic Gorbachev performance, of the
sort that had caused Andrei Gromyko to say of him:
'Comrades, this man has a nice smile, but he has teeth of
iron.'

*   *   *

At first glance, there was something puzzling about why Gorbachev would choose to show his iron teeth in Tyumen. After all, if there is one success story in the Soviet Union, it must be the energy sector: the Soviet Union is the world's biggest energy exporter and the biggest producer of oil and natural gas. Those production figures have made the Soviet Union the only major country in the developed world that is totally energy self-sufficient.[20] For anyone in the West who recalls the oil embargoes and petrol shortages of the early 1970s, the value of such a position is immediately clear. Because of this self-sufficiency in energy, the Soviet Union was insulated from the energy shocks of the 1970s.

Oil had long been an important export commodity for the Soviet Union. Even before the Revolution, in 1900, Russia produced half of all the world's oil, from fields around the Caspian Sea near Baku. Inevitably, as the world's demand for oil grew, new deposits were discovered elsewhere which cut the Soviet share of the world oil business, even though volume had dramatically increased. By 1983, Soviet wells produced more than one-fifth of all the oil pumped in the world, while all the Organisation of Petroleum Exporting Countries combined produced a third. In the same year, the Soviet Union produced thirty-five per cent of the world's natural gas, and production has been rising every year since. In addition to its huge production of oil and rapidly expanding natural gas production, the Soviet Union ranks third in coal production, behind only the United States and China.

This vast energy supply ensured that the Soviet Union became the world's leading exporter of energy. Before the 1973 Arab oil embargo and the start of the oil price spiral, Soviet energy exports produced about twenty per cent of the country's hard currency commodity earnings. But higher prices for hydrocarbons and increased Soviet production rapidly made energy exports an even more important part of the Soviet Union's international trade. In the last decade and a half, exports of oil and gas have become the principal source of hard currency, by some

estimates supplying up to eighty per cent of the approximately thirty billion dollars the Soviet Union earns from
exports. Despite seventy years of industrialisation, the
world's second biggest economy depends today on energy
exports to earn more than two-thirds of its hard currency
income.

During the 1970s, when the Organisation of Petroleum
Exporting Countries pushed world oil prices from around
five dollars a barrel to more than thirty dollars a barrel, the
hydrocarbon wealth of the Soviet Union seemed like a
blank cheque to pay for the imports of Western technology
that Brezhnev's planners counted on to modernise the
industrial side of the economy. And it financed the purchase of grain to make up for the continued failure of Soviet
agriculture to produce enough food for the country. With
the discovery of huge new gas deposits in West Siberia in
the 1970s, the Soviet Union found another hard currency
earner – a gas pipeline to Western Europe. The pipeline
became a hot political issue between the West Europeans
and the Soviets on one side and the Americans on the other
because the Americans worried that Europe could be
subject to Soviet energy blackmail. But by 1984, the pipeline was in operation and the Soviet Union was able to start
gas exports to the West.

An energy map of the Soviet Union shows huge deposits
of oil, gas and coal. Over the past three decades, oil and gas
have literally and figuratively fuelled the economy, as more
and more oil was pumped from the ground, more and more
gas sent down a rapidly growing network of pipelines. The
Soviet Union used its surplus of hydrocarbons to bind its
Eastern European allies ever more closely to it, by providing gas and oil at lower than market prices when OPEC was
ratchetting prices up.

An American Central Intelligence Agency study of
Soviet energy policy and prospects argues that 'the driving
force behind Soviet energy policy is Moscow's desire to
remain self-sufficient in energy while increasing hard currency earnings from energy exports.' Until recently, that

policy had appeared to be an unqualified success. But in the last few years, cracks began to appear in the façade.

First, there is the problem of where the resources are located. Until the 1960s, the Soviet Union drew most of its oil, gas and coal from the same area of the country where the fuels were used – the heavily populated European area west of the Ural Mountains. But years of exploitation of fuel deposits began to take their toll. As one recently published study of Soviet coal mining points out, the average depth of underground mines in the Soviet Union increased by twenty to thirty per cent every five years from 1960 to 1975.[21] Not only have miners had to dig deeper, but the coal seams that are being exploited are often narrower. A third problem is that the quality of the coal being mined is often not as high as earlier. In order to produce enough coal to fuel Soviet industry and generate enough electricity, new coal fields, most of them in the empty, harsh terrain of Siberia, have had to be developed. But this proved both costly and difficult.

If anything, the problem was more acute for the oil industry. In the decade from 1970, the cost of oil production nearly doubled, and the trend can only continue. This is because of the changing nature of Soviet oil production. The Soviet oil industry before the Second World War centred around the Caspian Sea, near Baku. In 1941, seventy per cent of Soviet oil came from the area around Baku. But after the war, the fields started to decline. Other fields – to the north of the Caspian Sea and in Soviet Central Asia – were developed. But it was the development of the Volga-Urals region, about 500 miles south-east of Moscow, that gave the Soviet Union its 'second Baku.'

The Volga-Urals oil region was almost too good to be true: much of the oil was in the big fields that the oil industry calls 'supergiants,' rather than in the smaller, less economical fields around the Caspian. And even better, the 200,000 square-mile region lay in the Russian heartland of the Soviet Union, near industries that would use the oil and the people to work in the oil fields. But production peaked in the Volga-Urals in 1975, when the region produced 4.5 million barrels of oil each day. Since then, the Volga-Urals fields have been in decline, and Western experts say they doubt that anything can be done to reverse the trend.

What saved the Soviet Union from the fate of other developed countries – reliance on OPEC – was the development of the West Siberian region around Tyumen. By 1978, West Siberia had surpassed the Volga-Urals in oil production and a year later, in gas production. Now, the region produces something like sixty per cent of all the country's oil and about fifty-seven per cent of natural gas. The Samotlor oilfield near Nizhnevartovsk went into production in the mid 1960s and by 1980 this one oil field was responsible for producing a quarter of all the oil pumped in the Soviet Union. Having such deposits was remarkable good luck, but the development of the fields, under conditions that are nothing less than extreme, was a major achievement and a source of continuing pride.

Nevertheless, the development of the new oil and gas fields, in inhospitable areas like the Tyumen Basin, or even farther north in the Siberian tundra, has been costly. Everything, including the people to do the work, must be brought in. The cost of building up all the support facilities is rising.[22] And, as the search for new sources of energy has moved to the East and North, away from the consumers, new strains have appeared. One of these is simply the problem of where the fuel – oil, coal or gas – is located. A private British study of the problem summed it up this way:

The fundamental problem is one of geography: 75 per cent of the country's population, together with the main centres of energy consumption, are located in the European part of the country, while 80 per cent of remaining energy reserves lie to the east of the Urals in areas of severe climate, difficult geology and poorly developed infrastructure.[23]

The Soviet energy problem is basically one of supply and demand. The dramatic increases in energy production have been more than matched by growing demand because of increased industrialisation and a failure to conserve energy adequately. Using more energy to produce more goods is the almost inevitable result of industrialisation, but Western energy economists say that the Soviet Union has failed to conserve energy, despite statements by top political leaders acknowledging the benefits of conservation.

Albina Tretyakova Birman, an émigré Soviet energy economist who now lives in the US, says that Soviet statistical handbooks show 'tremendous conservation.' But, she adds, those figures don't relate to reality.[24] However, even official statistics make clear the scope for improvement: in 1985, energy consumption per head was ten per cent higher in the Soviet Union than in West Germany, despite the fact that the West German economy produces twice as much per person as does the Soviet economy.[25] This is a clear sign of energy inefficiency.

A result of this continued failure to address the problem of conservation is that the energy sector eats up more than twenty per cent of all capital investment in the Soviet Union. Since agriculture takes up to a third of capital investment, that leaves less than half the total funds for modernising the Soviet economy and bringing to life Gorbachev's dream of an intensive, high-productivity Soviet Union.

* * *

If Soviet planners were concerned about energy generally, then concern was directly focused on one of the big users of energy – the production of electrical power. When Soviet energy planners look to the future, they worry about how they will be able to produce enough electricity to meet demand, about how they will move the fuel to run the power stations across the vast distances from Siberian reserves to the population centres of the west and about what they will do as the amount of easily-extracted fuel dwindles.

There have been massive strides in extending electricity supply. In 1920, the Soviet Union generated less than 500 million kilowatt-hours. In 1983, Soviet power stations generated 1.42 trillion kilowatt-hours, making the country the second biggest producer of electricity in the world, though far behind many industrialised states in power generation per person. To make these strides, as much as ten per cent of all capital investment in industry has been allocated to building power stations.

But it hasn't been enough. Particularly in the European Soviet Union, where people and industry are concentrated, power shortages are endemic. According to Albina Tretyakova, the controllers of Soviet electricity power grids have shut-off switches in their control rooms that enable them to turn off the power to selected factories when the grid is overloaded. This means that production lines can and do grind to a halt without warning.

The Central Intelligence Agency estimates that the power plants in the European Soviet Union produce about seventy-two per cent of the national output of electrical power. But the European region contains three-quarters of the people and most of the national industrial base – a sure recipe for shortages. With Soviet railways and pipelines already stretched to deliver fuel from increasingly distant mines and wells, and with continuing rises in demand, Soviet energy planners have long had to accept the fact that they have a real problem. And that problem has become worse, strangely enough, because of the fall in oil prices in the world market.

One reason for this is that in the 1970s, the Soviet Union became hooked on oil sales as a means of earning foreign exchange. When oil prices were high, it was easy to sell enough oil to earn the money needed for hard currency imports and foreign debt service. But when oil prices declined, Soviet hard currency needs did not. What this meant was that in order to earn the same amount of money, the country had to sell more oil. To make things worse, just as oil prices started to ease, the growth in Soviet energy production – except for natural gas – virtually halted.

The Soviet Union had a plan to resolve many of the problems in energy. Just as in the West, the answer to the energy problem seemed, only a few years ago, to be an alchemist's dream. In the United States, true believers spoke of a way to produce electricity that would make it 'too cheap to meter.' The true believers in the Soviet Union were just as enthusiastic. The answer seemed to hold out the promise of a bright new age by harnessing one of the elemental forces of nature – the energy locked inside the atom. The answer was nuclear power.

The Soviet Union claims to be the first country in the world to use nuclear power to generate electricity commercially. A demonstration plant in Arcon, Idaho, had performed the feat of producing nuclear-generated electrical power three years earlier, though the plant was not commercial. But Soviet nuclear scientists and engineers ushered in the commercial start of the nuclear power era on June 27th, 1954, with a five-megawatt reactor in Obninsk, south-east of Moscow. It was essentially a pile of graphite blocks, pierced by fuel channels, cooled by water – the same basic design as the 1000-megawatt reactors that powered the turbines at Chernobyl.

4

THE NUCLEAR ECONOMY

Mankind will acquire a new source of energy surpassing a million times everything that has hitherto been known . . . we shall have a fuel which will be a substitute for our depleting supplies of coal and oil and thus rescue industry from a fuel famine . . . man will be able to acquire any quantity of energy he pleases and apply it to any ends he chooses.

Izvestia, December 31, 1940[1]

The crucial year in the history of nuclear power was 1939. Working independently, a group of German scientists under the direction of Professor Otto Hahn and the French physicist Joliot-Curie demonstrated that it was possible to split, or fission, the uranium atom. A group of nuclear physicists who were holding a conference on theoretical physics in Washington were among the first to learn of the German experiment. The information came in the form of a telegram. One of the physicists who was in the room when the message was read out was the Russian émigré George Gamow. In a memoir of that event he wrote:

The possibility of a branching chain reaction and the large-scale liberation of nuclear energy seemed open. With the newspaper reporters politely shown out of the conference room, the pros and cons of fission chain reactions were carefully weighed. [Niels] Bohr and [Enrico] Fermi, armed with long pieces of chalk and standing in front of the blackboard, resembled two knights at a medieval tourney. Thus did nuclear energy enter the world of man, leading to uranium fission bombs, nuclear reactors and later to thermonuclear weapons![2]

Among the scientists, there was an almost instant recognition that if the atom could be fissioned, the possibility of self-sustaining nuclear reactions had become a reality. The way was opened to move from theory to practice. In more peaceful times, the physicists might simply have taken the new discovery in their stride and worked to develop the peaceful uses of nuclear energy. But 1939 was not a peaceful time. Emigré scientists from Hitler's Germany, many of them Jews who had fled persecution, warned that Hitler might well use the power of the atom to achieve his aim of world domination.

Within two years, the United States, Britain and Canada had launched the massive Manhattan Project of intensive atomic research that was to culminate with the explosion of atomic bombs over Hiroshima and Nagasaki, bringing the Second World War to an end. As a part of that research, Enrico Fermi and a team of scientists and engineers constructed the first working nuclear pile under the football grandstands of the University of Chicago in 1942.

During this period, atomic research became secret research, guarded as a national security secret. And suddenly, huge amounts of money and vast resources were funnelled into what had been, until recently, a subject of interest only to a few people who lived on a different intellectual plane from most of us. At that time, there was intense debate about whether a bomb could be built. There was even fear that if a bomb were set off, it might start a chain reaction that would engulf the whole world. And right up to July 16th, 1945, when the first experimental atomic bomb was set off in the deserts of New Mexico, some scientists believed that an unknown factor, not previously detected, would prevent explosion.

But the scientists were always sure that they could harness nuclear power to make electricity. What the Manhattan Project did was to accelerate vastly the development of nuclear energy technology, telescoping what might have been a process of decades of research into mere years. In that sense, nuclear power plants are the progeny of atomic bombs. The physics, the chemistry, the engineering that make nuclear power plants possible are the inheritance of the quest for the ultimate weapon. This is as true of the Soviet nuclear power programme as it is of the American programme. The first big nuclear reactors were built by both countries in order to burn uranium to make plutonium, the artificial element which makes the nuclear trigger for atomic bombs. The heat generated by the nuclear reaction was, for the early reactor builders, little more than a by-product, though the potential of the reaction for power generation was clearly recognised. And for nuclear physicists everywhere, unlocking of the secrets of the atom was accompanied by a closing of the channels of free exchange of scientific information.

In the four decades since J. Robert Oppenheimer, the scientific director of the American atomic bomb project, sat in the control room at the Trinity site in New Mexico and watched the 'radiance of a thousand suns' burst into the sky when the world's first nuclear explosion was touched off, much of the secrecy about the American nuclear programme has been stripped away. We know the story of the building of the bomb – the secret cities at Los Alamos, Hanford and Oak Ridge, the Manhattan Project itself and the agonised attempts of the physicists to put the nuclear genie back into its bottle after the war. The same is not true of the Soviet nuclear programme: more than forty years on, there is still comparatively little information about how, in the space of nine years, the Soviet Union created its own Manhattan Project, successfully exploded both atomic and hydrogen bombs and went on to produce a working nuclear electrical power station.

What is known is that the explosion of the atomic bombs

over Hiroshima and Nagasaki was the trigger for the huge Soviet nuclear programme that produced those results in the shattered and war-ravaged country.[3]

The man who led the Soviet nuclear effort was a Soviet physicist named Igor Kurchatov, who had first come to notice in 1925 when he became a member of the Soviet atomic commission, a group of academics who had originally organised in Petrograd (later Leningrad) in 1920 to try to coordinate atomic research in the Soviet Union. Before the war, in 1937, Kurchatov was the head of the team that built the first cyclotron in Europe. Two years later, a few months after the principle of nuclear fission was discovered in the West, a member of the Kurchatov team, G. M. Flerov, independently made the same discovery.

Soviet scientists were as quick as those in the West to realise the theoretical implications of that discovery. Peter Kapitza, the Soviet nuclear physicist who had worked at the Cavendish Laboratories at Cambridge University until Stalin refused to let him return to England in 1934, gave a publicly-reported lecture in 1941 in which he said that calculations proved that an atomic bomb could destroy a large city with 'several millions of inhabitants'. But according to a 1956 RAND Corporation study, the Soviet Union 'apparently dismissed the idea that [the bomb] would be feasible for the war then raging.' After stopping atomic bomb research, the Soviet Union again took it up in 1943. By the time the war was over, Kurchatov and his associates had worked out the theory of nuclear reactors and of atomic explosions, though they had not been able to move from theory to application.

The American explosions changed all that. The site for the Soviet Union's first nuclear reactor, the town of Obninsk about eighty miles north of Moscow, was chosen at the end of 1945 and the reactor was tested for the first time on December 25th, 1946. Stalin gave Kurchatov and the large team of scientists he gathered around him near-total freedom to mobilise the resources of the country. And in order to make sure that Kurchatov got what he wanted,

Stalin made the dreaded head of the secret police, Lavrenti Beria, the administrative officer in charge of the Soviet nuclear programme.

With this sort of support, Kurchatov moved quickly. He was assisted in this effort by the transfer to his control of all captured German physicists and by huge resources of slave labour from the *Gulag*. By 1947, the Soviet Union's first military reactor was completed and others had been started, all of them in secret cities. These secret cities were like the American ones in that no one could visit without clearance and there was no mention of them in the press. But they were different because they were a strange mixture of academic research facility and prison centre. It was necessary to use prisoners because so many Soviet scientists and technologists were incarcerated – victims of Stalin's continued efforts to blame failures in the system on wreckers, anti-Communists and collaborators. But these prisoners worked alongside free scientists, among them Andrei Sakharov, the man who would invent the Soviet hydrogen bomb. In his writings, Sakharov suggests that this experience was important in forming his dissident views.

In the West, of course, nothing was known of this huge effort, or of the methods by which it was being achieved. American military officials predicted that it might be as many as sixty years before the Soviet Union managed to make a bomb. Others – mostly scientists – were not so sure.

The massive Soviet effort paid off quickly, for by the end of 1948 or early 1949, the first plutonium from the new military reactors was being reprocessed, apparently at a plant that had been built in the Urals between the cities of Kyshtym and Chelyabinsk. In late August, American surveillance aircraft detected radioactive traces in the air that told them that the Soviet Union had caught up in the nuclear weapons race. And on September 23rd, 1949, President Harry S Truman acknowledged publicly that the Soviet Union had become the world's second atomic power. Less than a year later, tests began on deliverable atomic bombs.

Even as the work to make the Soviet Union into a fully-fledged nuclear weapons state surged ahead, the Soviet Union was also moving into the nuclear power field. In 1950, the decision to build a nuclear power plant at the research centre of Obninsk was taken and less than four years later, on June 27th, 1954, the plant was commissioned. From an economic point of view, it was not a great success, since it apparently used more electricity than it generated. But it did demonstrate that Soviet science was capable of advanced feats of technological achievement.[4]

*   *   *

By 1954, the United States and the Soviet Union – allies when the Americans dropped the bomb – were locked in the Cold War. Two years earlier, on November 6th, 1952, the United States had exploded the first hydrogen bomb on the Pacific atoll of Eniwetok. A year later, the Soviet Union followed suit, but with a bomb of a more sophisticated type. In 1954, the United States launched the world's first nuclear-powered submarine, the *Nautilus*.

Immediately after the war, western physicists, many of whom had contributed to the building of the atomic bomb, made a major effort to internationalise atomic energy, hoping to avoid an arms race and harness the power of nuclear fission for the benefit of the world. Before the bombs were dropped on the two Japanese cities, many of those same physicists and other scientists associated with the project to build the bomb had urged that it should not be used, among them Albert Einstein, who had played an important part in convincing President Franklin Roosevelt to authorise the Manhattan Project.[5]

After the bombs were used, the physicists did not give up. In the immediate aftermath of the war, many of the scientists urged that the American government should start talks with the Soviet Union about atomic matters. Their efforts were not appreciated by many military and political leaders, but they bore some fruit.

The first major attempt by the Americans to open talks with the Soviet Union on atomic energy was at the Four-Power Conference in Moscow in 1945. The distinguished American scientist James Conant was included in the US delegation with a brief to raise the subjects of exchange visits by nuclear scientists and international controls on atomic energy. But Soviet Foreign Minister Molotov refused to discuss the issue.

The United States, at the prompting of its own nuclear scientists, raised the issue again in 1946, with the publication of the Acheson-Lilienthal report, which called for international ownership and operation of all nuclear from uranium mines to research and production facilities. Later that year, the Americans presented to the United Nations Atomic Energy Commission a plan based on these proposals.[6] The Soviet Union's United Nations ambassador, Andrei Gromyko, rejected the plan in a speech on July 24th, 1946. From that moment on, the nuclear programmes of the two superpowers followed separate and secretive courses of development.

Of course, the United States and the Soviet Union were not the only countries with nuclear programmes. Britain and Canada had participated in the Manhattan Project, but post-war American secrecy efforts kept the full results of that work from them and both countries launched their own nuclear programmes. The British developed both civil and military programmes that culminated in the production of a British bomb in 1952, while the Canadians stuck to civilian applications. The French also created their own nuclear weapons. But despite the American secrecy, communications were never severed among the scientific communities of these countries, so today, the civil nuclear programmes of the Western states share much in common with each other. But that was not the case with the Soviet Union. Soviet nuclear science was cut off from interchange with the West during the crucial, early days when the outlines of the nuclear power programme were developed. In the immediate post-war period, the names of important Soviet nuclear scientists were themselves secret, and there was almost no opportunity for major scientists to make visits to their counterparts in the West, or to receive them in the Soviet Union. The scientists were a state asset, to be protected and hoarded.

Stalin's successor, Nikita Khrushchev, continued his predecessor's emphasis on the development of nuclear sciences, both military and civilian. He sought to use the achievements of Soviet nuclear scientists to bolster the prestige of the Soviet Union. One early example of this was the decision of the Soviet Union to participate in the first United Nations Conference on the Peaceful Uses of Atomic Energy in 1955. Contrary to the previous unwillingness to discuss nuclear matters, Soviet scientists did participate, delivering papers on a large number of subjects, revealing for the first time just how far Soviet nuclear science had progressed. The decision was in marked contrast with the lack of information in the Soviet announcement just a year earlier of the 'great success of the peaceful use of atomic energy' in the successful operation of a commercial power station, an announcement that did not even include the location of the station, Obninsk.

As the Cold War became less chilly, there was slightly more openness. The Soviet Union joined the International Atomic Energy Agency at its founding in 1957 and has participated in activities of the organisation ever since. By the early 1970s, during the period of détente, the practice of exchange visits and even cooperation on some joint projects developed, but by this time, the main patterns of the Soviet nuclear industry were set. Even during the period of closest contact between Soviet scientists and their Western counterparts, the level of exchange was far from the same enjoyed within the Western scientific and technological community. But that did not mean that the Soviet Union lagged behind in the effort to develop nuclear power.

* * *

Just as in the West, the Soviet Union has had high hopes for nuclear power from the earliest days of the atomic age. *Izvestia*'s 1940 New Year's Eve hymn of praise to the dawning nuclear age, '. . . man will be able to acquire any quantity of energy he pleases and apply it to any ends he chooses . . .,' is simply an early example of the consistently high hopes placed in nuclear power by its supporters, East and West.

In the early days of nuclear power, it seemed that the sky might truly be the limit for what could be done with the inexhaustible new energy source that had been unlocked. In the West, the public was told that nuclear energy could make electricity cost-free, that it might one day power aeroplanes and that nuclear explosives could be used to dig a new Panama Canal. Similar visions danced in the heads of Soviet engineers and scientists. The difference is that many of the schemes that the West abandoned, the Soviets carried on.

Soviet nuclear engineers had, as early as 1960, designed and operated a portable nuclear power plant which could be driven to remote sites on caterpillar treads. Once on the site, the reactor unit was to be driven into a trench and buried under concrete, while the control room and turbines were hooked up on the surface.[7] Three years later, another design team unveiled the ARBUS (Arctic Reactor Modular Facility), a nineteen-component nuclear power plant designed to be carried to any site where electricity might be needed, plugged together and simply turned on. Western scientists say that more recently, Soviet engineers have also produced truck-mounted nuclear power packs and a sort of neighbourhood nuclear power plant, the ABV 1.5. Designed for remote sites in extreme climates, the unit is said to produce enough power to heat as many as sixty apartment houses of ten flats each.

Another area where the Soviets persevered in a field largely abandoned by others is in the powering of non-military surface ships by nuclear power. In the United States, a demonstration ship, the *Savannah*, was supposed to be the prototype for a new generation of nuclear powered cargo ships, but the *Savannah* never proved economical or reliable. The Japanese launched their own nuclear-powered cargo liner, but abandoned it after a disastrous cruise that ended only when the crew managed to halt a leak of radioactive water by plugging it with a combination of the crew's socks and a wad of sticky rice.

The Soviet Union today operates a fleet of three nuclear-powered icebreakers. The world's first, the *Lenin*, went into operation in 1959. Two others, the *Arktika* and the *Sibir*, were launched in 1974 and 1977 respectively. One of the nuclear icebreakers' great advantages over ships powered with oil is that they don't ride up in the water as their fuel is burned. And, just as nuclear naval vessels can stay away from port much longer than conventional navy ships, so the icebreakers are free to remain at sea longer.

Perhaps, though, the most strikingly different use of nuclear power in the Soviet Union is the effort to heat cities with nuclear reactors. There is nothing remotely comparable in the West. Soviet figures show that about twenty per cent of all the fossil fuel burned in the country is used for central heating. That fact, and the difficulties that have been developing in the production and transportation of those fuels, illuminate the reasoning behind the scheme to construct nuclear-fired boiler plants on the outskirts of major cities.

Since 1973, a combined heat and electricity plant has been operating in the diamond-mining town of Bilibino, a settlement high above the Arctic Circle in the Siberian Far East. The Bilibino plant, which produces forty-eight megawatts, is about fifteen miles from the nearest settlement. A similar but larger combined power and heating plant is under construction outside the Black Sea port city of Odessa. Hot water pipes a yard in diameter will carry hot water to radiators in the city.

The unique development was the AST-500 nuclear boiler plant, designed to be built in cities. The idea of building nuclear reactors inside cities is an unusual one, to say the least. Construction on the first two of these plants started in 1982. One is located in Voronezh, about 300 miles south of Moscow and about 400 miles due east of Chernobyl. The other is in Gorky. The pressure vessel for the Gorky plant was shipped from the factory where it was manufactured in late 1985.

Soviet scientists, including the president of the Academy of Sciences, Anatoly Aleksandrov, have argued that nuclear boiler plants offer opportunities to conserve fossil fuel, cut down air pollution and save money, perhaps as much as a fifty per cent saving on the cost of fossil fuel. And Soviet nuclear experts have argued that the design of the plants, which operate at lower temperatures and pressures than electricity-generating nuclear plants, make them safe enough to build as close as a couple of miles from the edge of the city.

Despite these unusual features, the main thrust of Soviet civil nuclear engineering is the same as in the West – the production of electricity. The years after the start-up of the Obninsk power reactor were a period in which there was a considerable amount of experimentation with various types of reactors, as decisions were made about what design to develop. Not surprisingly, among the first reactors built were six of the graphite-block style constructions that constituted the Obninsk design. These reactors were built at Troitsk, in the eastern foothills of the Ural Mountains near Kyshtym. While they were mainly designed to produce plutonium for weapons, they also generated a total of 600 megawatts of electricity. In the early 1960s, there was little actual development of commercial nuclear power. At the end of 1965, the Soviet Union had ten operating commercial nuclear power units producing 962 megawatts of electricity. In 1970, the figure had grown to thirteen plants and nearly 1500 megawatts.[8] A long-time Soviet nuclear power expert, Boris Semenov, says that the major decision about the design of Soviet nuclear power reactors was taken in the late 1960s, when two reactor types were selected for commercial development.

The first of these was the VVER pressurised water reactor, a design similar to the pressurised water reactors of the West. The standard VVER produced 440 megawatts. The VVER-440 proved successful. In 1985, twenty-seven of them were operating in the Soviet Union and Eastern Europe and one VVER-440 plant was under construction in Cuba. The Soviet Union made its only sale to a non-Communist country when the Finnish publicly-owned utility bought two VVER-440s, which went into operation after modification to meet Finnish nuclear safety standards.

Based on the development of the VVER-440, Soviet designers scaled up the reactor and, in 1980, the first VVER-1000 – a 1,000-megawatt design – went into operation in Novo Voronezh. Since then, four more of the larger design have been put into operation.

The VVER reactors have a design that is basically similar to the Westinghouse pressurised water reactor – a core of uranium fuel rods is suspended inside a steel pressure vessel which is filled with water. The water, heated by the nuclear reaction of the fuel is drawn off and used to produce steam to drive turbogenerators. There are differences between the Soviet and Western designs, but the VVER is a reactor type which would be familiar to any Western nuclear engineer.

The Soviet designers did not choose only one design for development. The first Soviet reactors were graphite-block reactors, just as were the first Western ones. But unlike the West, the Soviet Union continued to develop graphite reactors. By 1970, they had started construction on what was, at the time, the biggest graphite reactor in the world, the 1,000-megawatt RBMK at a site near Leningrad.

Described at its simplest, the RBMK is a circular pile of graphite blocks, about twelve and a half yards in diameter and almost seven and a half yards high. The blocks are stacked up like a giant set of *Lego*. The pile of graphite weighs 1,700 metric tons.[9] Running through the blocks from top to bottom are circular channels, about four inches in diameter. All told, there are 1,872 channels. Of that total, 1,661 are fuel channels. The rest are channels for control rods or for the insertion of monitoring instruments. Each one of the channels in the reactor core is plumbed into the water cooling system. The uranium fuel that heats up the water is contained inside fuel assemblies that are themselves positioned inside these water pipes. The heat of the nuclear chain reaction is drawn off from the fuel assemblies and heats the water that is pumped through the channels. At both the top and the bottom of the reactor core, there are complex arrangements of water pipes that look a lot like the exhaust pipe headers that come out of the engines of racing cars. The core of the reactor is encased in an airtight steel box and rests on a massive steel support system, which itself rests on a concrete cruciform structure.

Western nuclear engineers say that the feature of the RBMK that is most impressive is the way that Soviet engineers have managed to weld the zirconium alloy pressure tubes to the steel headers. They say the techniques involved are a major metallurgical achievement. The fact that the reactor is made essentially by piling up blocks of graphite and then connecting pipes together makes the RBMK a relatively inexpensive and uncomplicated reactor to build. But the same features that make RBMKs easy to construct make them difficult to maintain: there are literally hundreds of thousands of pipe connections, any of which can spring a leak. So, just keeping track of all those potential leak points requires a massive leak detection system.

The RBMK has another feature that is unlike most other Western reactors – it is designed for what is known as on-line refuelling. In other words, the reactor can be fuelled even as it continues to operate. Most reactors have to be shut down to change the fuel, but these shut-downs mean that the unit is out of service, sometimes for months at a time. On-line refuelling capability is not a feature of most Western technology.

The ease of construction and the possibility of lengthy operating time between shut-downs means that the

RBMK-1000 has been, over the last fifteen years, the major contributor to the growth of nuclear power in the Soviet Union. In addition to the currently-operating four units at Leningrad, there are RBMK units at Kursk, Smolensk, Zaporozhe and, of course, Chernobyl. Excluding the Chernobyl reactors, the Soviet Union had eight operating RBMK-1000 reactors in 1986, two under construction at Smolensk and plans to build two more at Kursk.

The reactor designers have not been idle since the development of the RBMK-1000. Instead, they have been at work on a further refinement, the RBMK-1500, designed to produce half again as much power as the RBMK-1000 from a unit of the same size. The essential difference between the two units was a modification of the channel assemblies to allow more heat to be transferred to the cooling water. With higher heat transfer, the RBMK could produce more power, making the RBMK-1500 the world's most powerful reactor. The first of the new RBMK-1500 units went into service in Ignalina, Lithuania, in 1984, joined by a second unit in 1986. Two more RBMK-1500s are under construction and Soviet authorities have announced plans for six more of these big units.

In their writing about the RBMK reactor type, Soviet nuclear officials have singled out as major reasons for their attachment to this unusual design the ease of manufacture of the units; the fact that the reactor design means there are 'essentially no upper power limits;' the fact that a failure of a single cooling channel would not cause a catastrophic accident, and the fact that the reactor is an efficient producer of plutonium.[10] By examining the shape of the Soviet nuclear power programme, it becomes clear that this last characteristic of the RBMK is of particular significance.

*　　*　　*

In 1955, the Soviet Union placed into operation its experimental plutonium-fuelled reactor.[11] That event was significant because it marked the first success in the long-term goal of the Soviet nuclear industry: the development of nuclear reactors that generate their own fuel. Technically, this is known as closing the fuel cycle. But there is another phrase that is perhaps more apt – the plutonium economy.

Plutonium^{239} is an artificial element, which can only be produced by bombarding uranium with neutrons – a process that goes on inside nuclear reactors. If ingested, plutonium is among the most toxic substances known. As small a quantity as one millionth of a gram is believed capable of causing cancer. Like strontium, plutonium displaces calcium in mammal bones, so once plutonium is taken into the food chain, it stays there. Unlike many radioactive substances, it does not decay rapidly; the half-life of plutonium^{239} is 24,400 years. Plutonium is particularly useful for making bombs because it takes less plutonium to reach critical mass than uranium^{235}. That is why the earliest big nuclear reactors were dedicated to the production of plutonium to make bombs.

Plutonium also has characteristics which make it attractive to nuclear planners. Plutonium can be used to increase the potency of uranium in order to make it usable as reactor fuel. Even more appealing to nuclear planners is the fact that nuclear reactors of a certain design can be used to breed more plutonium, which can then be used to fuel more nuclear reactors and produce even more fuel. There is no magic about this. Instead, it has to do with the various forms of uranium – their Different Atomic weights. To make conventional graphite – or water-moderated reactors work, large quantities of uranium^{235} are needed, but uranium^{235} is far from the most common form of uranium. In its natural form, uranium is more than ninety-nine per cent composed of uranium^{238}, while uranium^{235} makes up less than three-quarters of one per cent. To make conventional thermal reactors work, a complicated process of enrichment is necessary in order to bring the concentration of uranium^{235} up to two or three per cent.

Enrichment is costly and among the most difficult of modern industrial processes. There is also the problem of scarcity: eventually uranium is going to run out, just as will petroleum and coal. Uranium – it is often forgotten – is a commodity, of which there may be as much in the world as tin or molybdenum.[12]

The Soviet Union and its allies do not openly discuss their uranium resources, so any estimate of how much uranium they have is necessarily speculative. However, one recent estimate of the known resources of uranium in the world placed the figure at about six million tons. Of that amount, only one million tons were believed to be located in the territories of the Soviet Union and its political allies, while two-thirds of the uranium resources were located in the United States or Canada.[13] According to a report prepared by the West German Federal Institute for Geosciences and Natural Resources, the known resources of uranium in all the so-called centrally planned economies might be as high as two million tons.[14] About seventy per cent of that total is thought to be located in Eastern Europe and the Asian part of the Soviet Union.

Eastern Europe has long been a centre of uranium mining. In Czechoslovakia, mining started in 1830 at the town of Joachimsthel, where uranium was mined for use as a pigment for glass. During the Second World War, mines in Silesia, now a part of East Germany, were the source of uranium for the small German nuclear weapons research programme. In the Soviet Union, uranium has been mined since 1900, originally from a deposit in Central Asia. Today, the main uranium mining centres are in the Ukraine, the North Caucasus and in Central Asia. By the mid-1970s, total Warsaw Pact uranium production was estimated at 17,500 tons annually, of which about 7,000 tons came from the Soviet Union.[15]

Since the end of the Second World War, the Soviet Union has sought to develop a major stockpile of uranium. Immediately after the war, the emphasis was on production from the Czechoslovak and East German mines. In both countries, use was made of forced labour in order to accumulate as rapidly as possible a supply of what had become a crucial strategic mineral. The production of uranium was organised under the Eighth Directorate of the Soviet Ministry for Medium Machine Building, the secretive organisation that makes Soviet nuclear weapons and controls all uranium supplies, both for civil and military purposes.

Because of the secrecy surrounding everything the ministry does, it is hard to be certain just how the Soviet Union views its supply of uranium. But it is known that there has been prospecting for uranium in the Black Sea, an area where, geologists say, the ores are likely to be of a low quality. In addition, there have been approaches by the Soviets to potential Western sellers of uranium, including both the United States and Australia. There have been rumours – hotly denied by the Soviet Union – of arrangements for uranium supplies from South Africa. In 1979, the Soviet Union signed a contract with Morocco for the purchase of large quantities of phosphate which contained a significant uranium content. The Soviet payment for the phosphate was to be made partially in oil.

In 1984, the trade journal *Nuclear Fuel* carried a report quoting Afghan resistance sources who claimed that the Soviet Union had begun mining uranium in Afghanistan and sending it back to the Soviet Union. The report was based on a claim by an Afghan defector named Mir Zaman Mohammad, who said he worked with a Soviet geological team at a mining project in the Khwaja Rawash Mountains as chief engineer in the gelogical survey of the Afghan Ministry of Mining and Industry. According to the report, the exports of ore started in late 1983. The magazine said that Soviet Embassy officials in Kabul had told a staff member they were not aware of significant uranium deposits in Afghanistan and that their country was not involved in any Afghan uranium mining schemes.[16] However, Western geologists point out that the area where the mine was reportedly located is geologically similar to areas north of the Afghan border where the Soviet Union does have mines.

As recently as 1979, the production of uranium in the Warsaw Pact countries may have exceeded demand by as much as 10,000 tons annually. And with a stockpile of uranium that has been estimated to be as high as 200,000 to 400,000 tons, the Soviet Union would seem an unlikely purchaser. So why have the Soviets been seeking out more uranium supplies? Several answers suggest themselves.

The first is simply that the uranium stockpile might be much lower than generally believed. Or, Soviet military requirements might have taken a larger share of production than had been thought. Another possibility is that there have been difficulties in developing new domestic reserves, many of which are located in Siberian regions at least as forbidding as the Tyumen oil fields.

It seems likely that the answer lies in the need to build up a stockpile of fuel. The mathematics are simple enough: to make up a reactor-load of 2.3 per cent enriched uranium fuel for the RBMK or a similar-sized pressurised water reactor – about 200 tons – requires at least 600 tons of natural uranium. The fuel will have to be replaced at least every three years. So each reactor consumes at least 200 tons of natural uranium each year. Thus, with only fifty reactors, 10,000 tons of natural uranium will be consumed annually. A rough calculation suggests that the 1985 requirement for natural uranium to fuel Soviet power reactors might well be about 5,000 tons. Since a massive expansion of nuclear power generation is planned for the coming decade, there will be more and more pressure on uranium supplies. It seems apparent that the Soviet Union remains concerned about securing adequate supplies of uranium, even in a period when there is a comparative glut of fuel in the world market. And one of the ways that the Soviet nuclear planners have chosen to maximise their uranium supplies is through the use of breeder reactors.

*　　*　　*

The beauty of the breeder reactor – in the nuclear planner's eye – is that it can convert uranium[238] into plutonium. And plutonium is just as efficient a reactor fuel as the rare uranium[235]. In theory, by the use of breeder reactors, it should be possible to get a hundred times more energy out of uranium than simply through burning it in thermal reactors.[17] According to Soviet nuclear official, Boris Semenov, who worked on the Obninsk station and has been involved in the Soviet nuclear power programme ever since, the Soviet authorities recognised from the very beginning that a large-scale, long-term nuclear power programme would depend on getting around the problem of limited supplies of uranium through the use of breeder reactors.[18]

This realisation is not unique to the Soviet Union. Until 1977, when President Jimmy Carter proposed the cancellation of the American breeder reactor project at Clinch River and an end to reprocessing of spent reactor fuel to separate plutonium, the United States was involved in development of breeder reactors and a closed fuel cycle.[19] In fact, the first nuclear electricity came from an American breeder reactor. Four years after this achievement, though, the reactor's core melted. An American fast breeder reactor near Detroit operated from 1966 to 1972 but never managed to produce commercial electric power. A partial meltdown of its core is reported to have led to consideration of the possibility of evacuating Detroit.[20]

Britain had an early involvement with breeder reactors. The Dounreay Fast Reactor produced commercial power from 1962 until it was shut down in 1978. The United Kingdom Atomic Energy Authority continues to operate another fast breeder reactor at Dounreay, which has been in commercial use since 1977.[21] France has the most active breeder programme in the West. The Phenix reactor has been producing commercial power since 1974, and the biggest breeder in the world, the 1,200-megawatt Super Phenix, was connected to the national electrical grid in

January 1986, and was to be brought up to full power later in the year. West Germany has a small fast breeder in operation and a larger one in the late stages of construction. The Japanese have started construction of a fast breeder power station, too. Both the Germans and the Japanese have said, however, that they do not see any immediate future for breeder reactors in nuclear power.

Nowhere has the concept of a closed nuclear fuel cycle using fast breeders to make plutonium been so whole-heartedly embraced as in the Soviet Union. From the 1955 experimental reactor, which ran on twenty-six pounds of plutonium, the next step was a 100-kilowatt reactor that was cooled by mercury and started operation in 1956. In 1959, a sodium-cooled 5-megawatt reactor was started up at the Institute of Physics and Power at Obninsk, followed just three years later by the commissioning, at the Atomic Research Institute in Dimitrovgrad on the Kuybyshev Reservoir, of a breeder that produced 12 megawatts of electricity.

The first fruits of this period of development came with the start-up in 1973 of the first Soviet commercial proto-type breeder reactor, the BN-350, at Shevchenko on the Caspian Sea. This reactor produces 121 megawatts of electricity and is used to desalinate 85,000 tons of sea water each day. In 1980, the commercial operation of a 600-megawatt BN-600 reactor at Beloyarsk in Tyumen Province was seen by Soviet officials as a major step toward the development of a fast breeder design for mass production. Plans have been announced for construction of two mass production models, the 800-megawatt BN-800 and 1600 megawatt BN-1600, both of which are reported to share design features with the BN-600.[22]

One leading international expert on nuclear fuel and nuclear power suggested in private conversation that the Soviet breeder reactor programme may well be driven today by the fact that so many top Soviet nuclear power officials have been involved with breeders over the years. The expert said he thinks that since these officials told the political leaders of the country that the breeder was the right choice for the future, they now have a vested career interest in seeing the breeder programme through. And, unlike the countries of the West, where a legitimate opposition to breeders developed, there is no alternative voice in the Soviet Union, where the legitimate voice is the official one.

Moving to a breeder-based plutonium economy requires a considerable stockpile of plutonium, for, although breeder reactors are called 'fast', that word has to do with the speed of the energy of the neutrons in the reaction rather than the speed with which the reactor produces plutonium. Fast breeder reactors do not produce plutonium rapidly: according to one recent estimate, the best fast breeders only produce about ten per cent more plutonium a year than they consume, which would mean that under ideal conditions it would take ten years of operation of one reactor to produce enough plutonium to fuel a second breeder.[23] In fact, most breeder reactor designs have net yields of seven per cent or less. The alternative to starting up a breeder with a plutonium fuel load is to use uranium[235] enriched to about seventy-five per cent. But that level of enrichment is extremely costly and renders the whole breeder reactor idea far from cost-effective.

A further problem with the plutonium economy is that there are real worries about the safety of breeder reactors. The French Super Phenix reactor, for instance, uses molten sodium as its coolant. Exposed to air, the sodium is spontaneously combustible, and, because it circulates in the reactor core, it is radioactive. The temperatures at which breeder reactors operate are much higher than thermal reactors, another factor that makes them inherently more dangerous. If a fast breeder should discharge its fuel into the air, the spread of quantities of plutonium across the landscape would produce an extremely toxic, extremely long-lived environmental outrage.

*   *   *

If the Soviet nuclear programme has gone farther down the road toward a plutonium economy than have most others, it still shares common problems with its counterparts. Among those problems is the growing length of time that it takes to get power plants into operation. According to Soviet information furnished to the International Atomic Energy Agency, the average time needed to construct a reactor in the Soviet Union has gone from fifty-six months in the years 1955–59 to 105 months in the 1980–85 period. In the later period, it took the United States 131 months to build a reactor and the British 242 months.[24] Everywhere, the growing scale and complexity of nuclear power plants has meant increasingly long lead times for construction. Of course, for both Britain and the United States, part of the reason for the delays is the access of citizens and environmental groups to legal proceedings that can bring a halt to construction. In the Soviet Union, the reasons for delay had more to do with industrial troubles.

Over the years, Soviet news media have reported on troubles in the construction of nuclear plants. A selection of those reports gives some idea of the sorts of problems that have plagued the industry.[25]

In 1980, *Radio Moscow* carried a broadcast complaining of deviations from design specifications at the Smolensk nuclear power plant, and the following year it reported that there were not enough skilled workers to do installation work, which had led to the employment of workers without proper qualifications. In 1982, the newspaper *Trud* reported that unrealistic construction schedules had been imposed at the plant – since 1979, work quotas had been increased four times. The following year, the same newspaper said that there were problems in getting the proper sort of concrete for the building. And in 1985, *Trud* complained that the plant designers had not furnished the constructors of the plant with the design documentation needed for work that was then going on.

The newspaper *Sotsialisticheskaya Industriya* has also reported extensively on problems with plant construction.

In 1982, the newspaper said that construction teams at the Rostov nuclear plant were not getting the equipment, supplies or manpower needed. And the situation was made worse when many of the Rostov workers were transferred to work on other nuclear plants at Chernobyl, Kursk and Orenburg. In 1982, the paper reported on violations of labour discipline and shortages of ferroconcrete and steel. After a series of construction mistakes, a special commission was sent to look into the situation. The commission refused to accept more than a quarter of the work presented for approval the first time and some work had to be re-done six times before it reached an acceptable standard.

At the Balakovo nuclear power plant, the newspaper *Sovetskaya Rossiya* reported in 1982, the steel pipe delivered to the site was 'absolute junk.' The next year, the same newspaper said that the plant was not getting enough supplies, while those that were coming through were of such quality that they were causing particular anxiety. By 1985, the paper reported, there seemed to be a problem among the various construction brigades at the site with some groups intent on demolishing what others had built. Pipe layers were singled out for 'destroying everything in their path.' A 1984 report in *Komsomolskaya Pravda* from Kursk told of how a construction boss ordered that defective concrete panels be installed because he was more concerned with fulfilling the plan than quality work. At the Odessa power plant site, according to *Radio Moscow*, poor planning caused delay. In 1986, one worker at the site told a journalist, 'We are hampered by incorrect planning: people live only for today; the Flood can come tomorrow for all they care.'

Perhaps the most telling story came from Kalinin, where a second generating unit was supposed to go on line in June, 1986. But because of equipment shortages, the plant staff were cannibalising the incomplete second unit in order to keep the first unit running. According to the newspaper *Stroitelnaya Gazeta*, the operating staff at the first unit was sneaking onto the construction site in the middle of the night to purloin parts needed to keep the first reactor going.

In addition to the problems at the construction sites, the Soviet nuclear programme has been hampered by a major setback at the manufacturing plant that is supposed to mass-produce the Soviet 1,000-megawatt VVER pressurised water reactor. The Atommash plant, in the specially-built new city of Volgodonsk, in southern Russia, was supposed to turn out its first reactor in 1978 and produce four reactors a year until completion of the second stage of building when it was to produce eight VVER-1000 reactors and ancillary equipment.[26]

The plant has never lived up to that aim. Almost from the first, it was plagued with trouble, with reports of construction difficulties due to poor construction documentation. The Soviet Ministry of Power and Electrification was blamed for failing to provide adequate financing for the plant and failing to cope with the tasks before the ministry. The first stage of construction at the plant was completed in 1979, and the following year the plant's director told touring Western journalists that the first reactor would come off the production lines in February 1981, and that another would be ready by December 1981 – a production schedule of just more than one a year rather than the four planned. Subsequently, there were more delays in construction of the second phase of the plant, in part because of inadequate supplies of structural steel. The problems continued until some time in 1983, when real disaster struck the four billion dollar plant.

According to Western press reports appearing at the time, because of a bad decision to locate the Atommash plant on the shores of an artificial lake, the foundations of the plant suffered such severe erosion that some sort of industrial accident took place. Whatever the exact sequence of events, it was so serious that a number of top Soviet officials flew in to look at the plant and had scathing comments to make about the way the project had been built. Several high-ranking officials, including a deputy prime minister in charge of heavy construction and the chairman of the State Committee for Civil Construction, were dismissed from their jobs over the Atommash débacle.

By 1985, the collapsing foundation of the plant apparently had been repaired and partial production had been started on the assembly line. But the ambitious plan to build eight VVER-1000s a year apparently had been cut back to only four or five units, enough to meet the demands of the current five-year plan but far from the goal set when the plant was started.

* * *

If construction problems and design difficulties have slowed down the development of Soviet nuclear energy, one thing that has not affected the ambitious plans for increasing nuclear power generation is the Soviet Union's previous big nuclear disaster, the so-called Kyshtym accident.[27]

The accident apparently took place either in late 1957 or early 1958 in the southern Ural Mountains. Several alternative explanations of what happened at Kyshtym have been offered. One suggestion is that one of the Soviet military plutonium reactors went out of control. There was a suggestion that a nuclear fuel reprocessing plant, where plutonium for weapons was being separated from spent nuclear fuel, suffered a chemical explosion. Another explanation is that improperly buried nuclear wastes concentrated in their burial vault and that a 'mud volcano' of highly radioactive material exploded when the wastes produced a spontaneous nuclear chain reaction. There are other explanations, too, but they are all speculative, since thirty years later, there is still no official acknowledgment that the accident ever happened.

In any case, the results of the Kyshtym disaster were staggering. According to the former Soviet biologist Zhores Medvedev, who revealed the accident to the West:

Tens of thousands of people were affected, though the real figure has never been made public. Probably many hundreds died quickly, thousands more slowly, and the full impact of the tragedy will probably never be known.[28]

Most estimates of the scope of the disaster speak of an area of hundreds of square miles being so contaminated by radioactivity that even now, large parts of the region are off-limits, and a dozen villages have simply disappeared from the map. After the accident, a sign along a twenty-mile stretch of the Chelyabinsk–Sverdlovsk road warned travellers to pass through quickly with car windows closed – presumably to avoid radioactive contamination.

The West learned almost nothing of the accident until Medvedev published an account of it almost twenty years later in 1976, in the British weekly, *New Scientist*. He followed this article in 1979 with a book, *Nuclear Disaster in the Urals*, in which he showed that Soviet scientists had written a number of thinly-disguised books and articles about the environmental damage.

Kyshtym is not believed to be the only Soviet nuclear accident prior to Chernobyl: less serious incidents involving leaks of radioactivity are believed to have occurred in 1974 at Shevchenko and in 1981 at Rovno. But from what can be pieced together, the accident in Kyshtym apparently was the world's biggest peacetime nuclear disaster – at least until April 26th, 1986.

5

PREPARATIONS FOR MELTDOWN

The Chernobyl accident resulted from a combination of several unlikely events. The Soviet Union is drawing the appropriate conclusions from the accident.

USSR State Committee on the
Utilisation of Atomic Energy[1]

More than six years before the reactor at Chernobyl blew up, there was a serious nuclear accident at another Soviet RBMK reactor. The accident happened in January 1980, at a nuclear power station in the city of Kursk, about 250 miles west of the Chernobyl power station. At the time the accident was not made public. Only in the aftermath of Chernobyl have even a few details been released in the West. What happened?

According to an official Soviet report, one of the RBMK units at the Kursk nuclear power plant completely lost electrical power without warning. The huge pumps that circulate more than ten million gallons of water an hour through the reactor at a temperature nearly three times that of water in a boiling kettle failed, leaving the reactor without its normal cooling system. The accident happened when the reactor was running at about thirty-five to forty per cent of its full power. Though the accident was a major one – 'one of the most severe accident situations that can occur' – it did not become known, and then only in bare outline, until more than six years after it took place.[2]

The Soviet report on the Kursk incident said this 'most severe' accident did almost no damage. Reactor power did not rise despite the drop in cooling, and there was no damage from overheating. Natural circulation of cooling water kept everything under control. The Soviet report acknowledges that the flow of cooling water dropped to about twenty per cent of normal during the accident. According to the Soviets, the accident showed that the plant design was a good one, demonstrating that 'reliable and safe' operations of the RBMK reactor could be assured if a loss-of-electricity accident took place at low power. However, not everyone who has studied the Kursk accident is so sure.

An international group of nuclear safety experts who studied the Chernobyl accident have expressed interest about the Kursk accident. They acknowledge a Soviet claim that during the whole time RBMK reactors were operating before Chernobyl, there was no event that could be considered a precursor for the events of April 26th. But then they add, 'however, the Soviet interpretation of "precursor" may be different from that used elsewhere.' The experts note that:

The events at the Kursk station . . . would be extremely interesting for examining some of the important . . . characteristics of the Chernobyl station.[3]

The Soviet experts who wrote the report on Chernobyl insist that RBMKs have had an excellent safety record. Evaluating this claim is difficult because the Soviet Union has never acknowledged any major accidents in its nuclear power industry. One official of the International Atomic Energy Agency said that the Soviet authorities have never made a formal notification of any severe accidents at nuclear power stations, despite the Soviet Union's membership in the IAEA Incident Reporting System. So why did the authors of the Soviet report choose to include information about a hitherto unknown accident involving a reactor system that was already suspect?

A Swedish nuclear safety expert who has studied

the small amount of information made available about the accident believes the Kursk event was a signal that the RBMK reactor had 'a safety deficiency in some situations.' The expert, Per Persson of Swedish Utilities, said he believed that the Kursk accident may have motivated the ill-fated experiment that produced the Chernobyl disaster. According to Persson, the 1980 accident would have provided 'some warning' about a safety deficiency in the RBMK reactor design.[4] Persson said that the details of the Kursk accident in the Soviet report suggest that there was concern about the Kursk accident – concern that may well have been the trigger for the series of events that eventually led to the Chernobyl disaster.

*   *   *

Whether it was the Kursk accident or some other as yet unrevealed development, it is known that in the years after 1980, Soviet nuclear experts became concerned about the potential for a dangerous loss-of-coolant accident if an RBMK reactor lost the electrical power needed to operate its cooling pumps and other emergency systems. Soviet authorities have acknowledged that there are some essential safety systems of the RBMK reactor which 'cannot tolerate an interruption in power supply . . . and for which a power supply is absolutely essential' after an emergency shutdown of the reactor and a second group of systems that cannot do without electricity for periods of time longer than 'tenths of a minute' and which are also essential to safety.[5]

In order to provide continuous electrical power, nuclear power plants have four separate sources of supply. The first of these is the electricity that is generated by the plant itself. Only a tiny fraction of that power is necessary to run the pumps and electrical equipment of the plant. This is the normal source of electricity. A second source of supply is the power grid to which the station is connected; in other words, the power station can draw on power from elsewhere in the system. But switching over to the grid is not a task that can be accomplished immediately. So two emergency back-up systems are provided.

At RBMK plants, power for systems that must never lose electricity (such as the computer that operates the central monitoring system and control devices) can be drawn from batteries that are kept charged and can provide enough electricity to keep instruments running for some time. But for the cooling water pumps, the pressurisation system and other big users of electricity, batteries are not a realistic answer because these systems require more electricity than batteries can realistically be expected to provide. The plants are equipped with big diesel-powered generators to produce large amounts of emergency power. But, like the engines in diesel cars, the diesel generators do not reach full power immediately. Based on the Soviet report and comments made to Western technical experts by Soviet nuclear power officials, it appears that it may take as long as fifty seconds for the back-up diesel generators to come up to full power – considerably longer than European and American designs. The evidence provided by the Soviet authorities suggests that someone – perhaps an official of the Ministry of Electrification – was worried that the response time of the diesels was too slow for safety in an emergency. So experiments were ordered to try to find a way to bridge the gap between the time of a power failure and the achievement of full power from the diesel standby generators. One of these experiments – prompted by fears about the performance of the reactor design – caused the Chernobyl disaster.

To understand these experiments, it is first necessary to understand how the reactor produces electricity. That requires a step back, to the first principles of nuclear power for electricity production.

The production of electricity is achieved in almost all power plants by using a turbine to spin a generator. This is true no matter what the source of power for the turbine. And most turbines in power plants are themselves driven by high pressure steam. It is in the means used to produce that steam that nuclear power plants are different from conventional oil, gas or coal power plants. In conventional plants, the oil or coal is burned under a boiler and the steam used to drive the turbine. But in nuclear power plants, the heat to produce steam comes from the splitting of atoms of uranium. This splitting is called fission.

As fission takes place in the reactor, a lot of heat is generated. The Chernobyl reactor was designed to operate with the graphite blocks that hold the fuel rods in place at a temperature of a maximum of 750 degrees centigrade. In order to draw off this heat, the reactor is cooled with water that is piped through the reactor. In the reactor, the water is heated to a temperature of nearly 300 degrees centigrade. The superheated water produces steam to run the turbines which generate electricity.

In the Chernobyl plant and others like it, each reactor makes enough steam to spin two 500-megawatt turbogenerators. These are huge machines, each one weighing 1,200 metric tons. When they are in operation the turbines spin at 3,000 revolutions per minute.[6]

It was realised after the Kursk accident that the huge mechanical energy stored in a spinning turbine might provide the needed source of power in the critical moments after a power failure. The turbine would keep spinning even if the supply of steam dropped off after a loss of pressure when the water pumps quit. If a way could be found to use that mechanical energy to keep the generator spinning, even at a lower level of power, the gap between the loss of electricity and the moment the diesel generators reached full output could be bridged. Experiments were ordered to test this theory.

Soviet officials have said that these experiments were carried out on RBMK plants in 1982 and 1984. According to the Soviet report, tests had been carried out at the Chernobyl plant itself, but without the hoped-for success. What happened was that the voltage produced by the spinning generators dropped much faster than had been anticipated. Electrical engineers were set to work on the problem and they thought they had found the solution, a new regulator that would help to keep the voltage from dropping. Now, they were ready to put their new device to the test. The engineers were told they could try out the new regulator on April 25th. And with this seemingly routine approval, events were set in motion that were to end in tragedy.

* * *

The events of April 25–26th at the Chernobyl Atomic Power Station would later be described in the official Soviet report of the accident as 'a violation of the most important provisions for safety.' But that was an evaluation made in retrospect. In the hours before the accident, the experiment planned for Chernobyl No. 4 seemed simple enough. According to the Soviet report of the accident, the reactor was due to be shut down for scheduled maintenance.[7] The unit had most probably been operating at nearly full power for months in order to provide the electricity needed to keep the Ukraine running during the winter months. Now, with the onset of warmer weather, the unit could be given a rest.

There was a final item of business: the experiment. The plan was that the reactor would be taken out of service on the power grid, power reduced, the experiment performed and then the reactor would be shut down. The experiment was outlined in a document titled 'Working Programme for Experiments on Turbogenerator No. 8 of the Chernobyl Nuclear Power Plant', a bland title that does not even hint at any involvement of the reactor.

According to the Soviet post-mortem report on the accident, the experimental programme 'was not properly prepared and had not received the requisite approval.' The programme included only a 'formal' nod toward safety factors. Because the question of safety was not properly considered, the report says, the staff at the reactor 'were not adequately prepared for the tests and were not aware of the possible dangers.' Supervision of the entire plant during the time of the experiment was not under the control of a nuclear expert but rather in the hands of an electrical engineer, who, the report says, 'was not a specialist in reactor plants.'[8] Thus, even before the experiment began, the ingredients for trouble were lying close to hand.

The electrical engineers had rigged their new voltage regulator in place for the test. The idea was to see if with the new regulator the turbogenerators could manage to keep spinning long enough to power the emergency core cooling system pump until the diesels were up to full power. When the experiment had been tried before, it had not worked, but there were hopes that the new regulator would solve what was considered to be simply a problem in electrical engineering. The engineers were not sure exactly how the new design would work and had come up with three or four different configurations to test. The experimental programme under which they were working called for the test to be done as a part of the shut-down of the unit, but the engineers wanted to retain the option to do more than one test – a planned violation of the approved programme.

Just after midnight on April 25th, the preparations for the experiment began with a slow power reduction in the reactor. Bringing the power down slowly is better for the reactor than a sudden drop in power because of the possibility of thermal shock if temperatures fall off too rapidly. By 1.30 in the afternoon, the reactor had been brought down to half power, and the No. 7 turbogenerator unit was shut down, leaving the No. 8 turbogenerator – the one to be used in the test – still producing about 500 megawatts of electricity.

Although the test was designed to see if power could be found to run the emergency core cooling system pump, the experiment did not call for starting the pump. Instead, the electrical load from the pump would be simulated by the regular water circulating pumps. The electrical engineers who were in charge of the test ordered that four of the pumps be connected to the power output of the No. 8 turbogenerator and the other four hooked up to the electrical supply from the power plant substation, which was driven by the other three reactor units at the plant. When the experiment was ready, the pumps hooked to the turbogenerator would be switched on.

The emergency core cooling system, which would normally be triggered by the experiment, was switched off. Switching off the system was specified in the experimental programme. But for reasons that even now remain unexplained, the system was shut down long before the experiment was performed. Shortly after the emergency core cooling system was switched off, a message came for a halt to preparations for the experiment.

The reason for the delay in the experiment was that the power from the remaining turbogenerator – 500 megawatts – was needed for the power grid. So, even though prior permission had already been given to do the test, everything was put on hold for nine hours, during which time the No. 4 unit made its contribution to keeping the lights of the Ukraine burning. The emergency core cooling system, however, was not switched back on. Though the failure to restart a basic safety system did not apparently contribute to the accident, it shows clearly how little the plant staff were concerned about safety. Why?

One Western nuclear physicist, who spoke to us privately, said that it is important to get a sense of 'how tired and exhausted people become' during experiments like the one at Chernobyl. This man, who directs reactor experiments himself, said that he will not allow an experiment to be scheduled on a Friday, because there is too much pressure to get the experiment over so that the staff can start their weekend.

The experiment at the Chernobyl station was scheduled for a Friday. But because of the demands of the grid controller, the experiment was still on hold. The Soviet report on the accident says that the control room staff shift had changed as normal. But the people who were running the experiment apparently remained at the plant for long dreary hours of waiting. The Western physicist put the situation in earthy terms:

> [The experimenters] work like hell to set up a test on time and then some asshole in Kiev makes them sit on their thumbs until one o'clock the next morning. . . . You almost need to sit through a major test to see what a tremendous bite in the ass all this preparatory folderol is.[9]

Finally, at 11 p.m., another call came through to the control room. As night deepened and factories shut down, the demand for power was lower and the network no longer needed the electricity from reactor No. 4. The test could go on.

The control room is the brain of the complex plant, but it is hard to find, hidden away in the third level of the massive power plant building. The building that housed the Nos. 3 and 4 reactors and their turbines was as wide as a football pitch and as long as four pitches. But it was from the control room and from the floor of the turbine hall that the test was directed.

When the signal was given to go ahead, one of the operators transferred the control of the reactor's power level from one system to another, but he failed to programme the new system with an instruction to maintain power at the minimum safe operating level. This error initiated the chain of failures that led to the accident. To see how crucial this failure was, it is necessary to understand something about how nuclear reactors work.

*   *   *

What makes reactors work is the fact that uranium[235] is unstable and that atoms of uranium[235] have a tendency to break up. This process of breaking up is called fission. When fission occurs, two things happen: first, energy is released, and, second, some of the neutrons in the fissioned atom fly off on their own. Fission can be thought of as a form of decay. And just as decay in a compost heap gives off heat, so does nuclear fission. The function of nuclear power reactors is to produce a controlled rate of fission. The goal is to use the heat that is released by fission to produce steam to run the turbogenerators that make electricity.

If one of the neutrons that has escaped from a fissioned atom hits another atom of uranium, it can cause that atom to fission, too. This is what is known as a chain reaction. Producing a chain reaction is roughly analogous to lighting a fire. But it is not enough to simply make a pile of uranium under a tank of water and wait for the water to boil. In order to work, nuclear reactors must be carefully designed so that they produce the right amount of fissions but not too few or too many. Reactor designers use particular features of the way that uranium fissions in order to control the reaction. One of the most important features is the way that the neutrons behave during fission.

When an atom of uranium fissions, some of the neutrons fly off at great speed, because they are full of energy. Others move more slowly. Some of the neutrons leave the atom at the instant of fission, while others take longer to depart. The differences in energy levels and time of departure are used by reactor designers to control the chain reaction.

The first point to understand is that the neutrons that travel at slow speeds are better at creating additional fissions than are the fast neutrons. So reactors are made, in part, of substances that can slow down the fast, high-energy neutrons. These substances are called moderators. What these moderators do is to absorb some of the energy in the fast neutrons so they are more likely to cause fission in other atoms.

Reactor designers know they must not allow too many fissions to take place because that would cause the chain reaction to go out of control. An out-of-control reaction would produce so much energy that the reactor would blow up. The designers use the fact that the neutrons leave the fissioned atoms at different times in order to keep the chain reaction from going out of control. The idea is to make sure that just enough neutrons hit other atoms so that the chain reaction keeps going but does not speed up too much. What the designers attempt to do is to make sure that it takes both the neutrons that leave the atom at the time of fission and the delayed neutrons in order to keep the chain reaction going. When the reaction is kept going in this way, it is called the 'just critical' state.

What happens if the balance between the production of neutrons and the number needed to keep the reaction 'just critical' is disturbed? If the number of neutrons produced is greater than the number needed for maintaining a steady 'just critical' reaction, then the power – the heat – produced by the reactor goes up. If the number of neutrons falls below the level needed to keep the reaction going, then the power of the reactor falls. This is how reactors are turned off – by inserting neutron-absorbing control rods, thus causing the chain reaction to slow down and stop.

On the other hand, the reaction can be sped up by removing control rods. But control rods are mechanical devices and do not operate instantaneously. And this is where the difference between the neutrons that leave the atom promptly and those that are delayed is essential. If the 'prompt' neutrons alone are sufficient to keep the reaction going, the reaction is no longer under control. In reactor jargon, this is known as 'prompt criticality'. Good reactor design means, in part, designing out the possibility of the reactor becoming 'prompt critical.' The choice of materials and the layout of the reactor core are the determining factors in avoiding 'prompt criticality.'

The Chernobyl reactor used graphite to slow down, or moderate, fast neutrons. Graphite is nothing more than carbon – the same stuff that is in the centre of a pencil. And graphite is good at slowing down neutrons.

The RBMK has control rods made of boron carbide

which were designed to make sure that not too many slow neutrons are available for fission.[10] These control rods can be inserted into the reactor. When inserted, they capture neutrons and slow down the reaction. If they are pulled out, more neutrons hit the uranium fuel and the reaction speeds up. When the control rods are inserted, the effect is similar to smothering a fire. When they are removed, the fire flares back up.

Graphite and boron carbide: one to slow down the neutrons, the other to absorb them. But there is a third element in the physics of the RBMK – water.

Water is an ambivalent factor in reactor designs. It can be a moderator or it can be an absorber. The design of the reactor determines which function is dominant. In the most commonly used design for nuclear power stations, the pressurised water reactor, water is the coolant and the moderator. In the Chernobyl-style reactors, water is used as the coolant and the working fluid. The water also absorbs some neutrons, thus tending to slow down the reaction. In the Chernobyl design, there is not enough water in the core for it to be an important moderator. This is an essential difference between the pressurised water reactor and the Chernobyl-style graphite reactor.

The importance of this difference is that in pressurised water reactors, if the water is removed from the core, then fewer neutrons are moderated, and the chain reaction slows down. But with the RBMK, the loss of water from the core means that fewer neutrons are absorbed, but the number of moderated neutrons remains the same, so the reaction may speed up. In other words, the Chernobyl-style RBMKs have been knowingly designed so that under some conditions if the amount of cooling water in the reactor falls, the power produced by the reactor rises because fewer neutrons are being absorbed.

In general, there are two circumstances in which the water level in the RBMK reactor might decrease to a dangerous level. One of them would be if the reactor's cooling water system ruptured. The designers of the

RBMK considered this to be the most dangerous sort of accident they could imagine and they designed a safety system to cope with it – the emergency core cooling system, which was shut off during the experiment. The other reason why the water level in the reactor might suddenly drop would be if for some reason steam production in the reactor increased. Steam bubbles – the reactor designers call them voids – are much less dense than water, so fewer neutrons would be absorbed by the steam than by the same volume of liquid water. Development of voids would mean that the number of neutrons available for producing fissions would be greater, so the level of power would go up. A reactor in which an increase in power leads to an increase in reactivity is said to have a 'positive coefficient of reactivity.' It is a generally agreed principle of reactor design that a positive coefficient of reactivity, particularly one brought on by steam voids, is something to be avoided. The RBMK has an exceptionally high positive void coefficient.

The RBMK is not the only reactor in the world with a positive void coefficient – the Canadian CANDU reactor is another. The now-cancelled Clinch River Fast Breeder Reactor that the Americans planned to build was another. In fact, the CRBR's positive void coefficient was one of the major factors in the programme's cancellation. But neither the CANDU nor the CRBR design has a positive void coefficient anywhere near the size of the RBMK. Western reactor designers consider a big positive void coefficient a major safety flaw to be designed out of reactors. That is because a positive void coefficient could lead to a reactor becoming 'prompt critical,' or out of control.

In the early days of the development of nuclear power generation, the United States set up a test site in Idaho to work out the problems of converting nuclear power into a workable technology. And one of the big concerns that the researchers had to deal with was the problem of how to make sure that if an accident happened to a reactor the chain reaction would not go out of control. To do this, the researchers deliberately tried to produce reactor accidents, including meltdowns. By the time they had finished their research in the 1960s, Western reactor designers were confident they could design reactors that would not grow more powerful if they lost their coolant. They maintained that they had found out how to build reactors in which the positive coefficient of reactivity did not pose a danger. In the Soviet Union, the danger posed by reactors with positive coefficients of reactivity was apparently dealt with in a different manner – not so much by design as by regulation.

In his article on nuclear power in the Soviet Union, the Deputy Chairman of the State Committee on the Utilisation of Atomic Power, Boris Semenov, acknowledged this approach when he wrote that 'the regulation of safety by official documents is one of the main tools for ensuring the safety of nuclear power plants in the USSR.'[11] It is an approach that is considered old-fashioned in the West and one which demands that operators of nuclear power plants exercise their skills constantly.

A similar willingness to trust both machinery and the people who operate it shows up in the way Soviet reactor designers approached the issue of reactor containment, a subject which was to become the focus of considerable controversy in the days after April 26th.

In their approach to reactor design, the Soviets set out to imagine the worst accident they could think of – the design basis accident. In the RBMK, they decided that the design basis accident was the rupture of the 36-inch pipe that supplied cooling water to the reactor. If that pipe burst, huge quantities of highly-pressurised, superheated, radioactive water would spew out. So they built a containment compartment for the cooling system, a structure designed to withstand pressure up to 4.5 times that of the normal atmosphere. They thought that in the core of the reactor itself, the worst that could happen would be for one of the more than 1,600 cooling water pipes to rupture, so they designed another containment structure for the reactor: but because only one pipe could rupture, the structure was built only to withstand just under twice the normal atmospheric pressure.[12] According to the design specifications, the Chernobyl reactor was safe.

One Western nuclear engineer who has studied the RBMK used this analogy to explain the safety strategy that seemed to govern it:

He said if one built a house on a hill, there were different ways to construct the entrance. One possibility would be to build a set of steps, protected by a railing, well-lit at night, smoothly finished, designed to take account of the failings of the people who would use the steps. Another possibility would be to put a ladder at the front door and to mark the ladder with a warning sign. Used properly, the ladder would be just as safe as the steps. But rushing down the ladder without caution could lead to danger.

If operators followed the rules for running the RBMK, the engineer said, it was safe. But what if they didn't follow the rules? And what if the designers had failed to anticipate the worst that could happen?

*   *   *

On April 25th, as the preparations for the experiment progressed, the reactor operators at Chernobyl were not worrying about power surges or positive coefficients of reactivity – they were worried about keeping the reactor running. The signal from the grid controller allowing the reactor to go out of service had come through just after 11 p.m. An hour and a half later, at 12.28 a.m. on April 26th, one of the operators made an error in the control room while switching the reactor from one control system to another – he failed to order the control system to keep the reactor at a steady power level. Because of this error, the heat output of the reactor started to decline rapidly, falling to less than one per cent of its normal power.

The effect of this decline in power was to make the water inside the reactor cooler. Because the water was cooler, it produced less steam and the space in the cooling channels that had been taken up by steam was filled with water. Since in the RBMK water acts as an absorber of neutrons, the increased water level meant that more neutrons were absorbed, causing even further reductions in power.

The operator's problem was compounded by the fact that there were now eight pumps feeding water to the reactor core. Even at full power, the reactor only requires the volume of water produced by six pumps, but the test programme called for all eight pumps to operate, forcing an unsafe volume of water through the reactor. The operator had another problem, too – the reactor was being poisoned by its own waste product, a radioactive gas called xenon.

Xenon is produced as a by-product of fission. The gas is chemically inert, but it does absorb neutrons. The higher the power in the reactor, the more xenon is produced. By the time that the go-ahead for the experiment came, the reactor had been running at half-power for many hours, so the level of xenon in the reactor was fairly high. Because of the wish to get the long-delayed experiment over, the operator attempted to reduce power too rapidly to the much lower level required for the experiment. As a result, the excess xenon absorbed even more neutrons.

In order to compensate for the absorption of neutrons by the water and the xenon, the reactor operator withdrew control rods, violating a basic safety rule for the operation of the RBMK. Pulling the control rods was dangerous because the removal of the rods increased the potential for the development of a power surge in the reactor; if for some reason the water level in the reactor should drop, the absence of the rods would mean that there would be less absorption of neutrons than normal. And with more neutrons producing more fissions, there was the possibility of a power surge developing.

Amazingly, the operator compounded his errors by increasing the flow of water to the reactor, adding even more absorption capacity and requiring even more control rods to be removed. At this point, automatic safety systems should have shut the reactor down, but the operator again defeated the safety systems by turning them off. The operator seems to have been obsessed with completing the experiment, totally heedless of the risks he was running.

What makes all this even more puzzling is the fact that the team that was operating the reactor was considered to be among the best. Unit No. 4 had operated without trouble for three years, and the unit had the best record of any RBMK in the country.[13] One Western expert who talked to the Soviet team who went to Vienna to brief the IAEA* on the accident put it this way:

> The operators of unit four were stars – award winners. They were asked to do a test and they were going to do it. There was a chance the first test might fail, [but] there were alternate arrangements so if at first it failed, you could try again. But to try again, you had to keep the reactor running. Were it to trip off, you wouldn't be able to restart until the xenon decayed out. These guys were going to get the job done.[14]

The problem was that in order to get the test done, the operators were taking risks. And those risks were growing in an almost geometric progression. By now, Chernobyl was only minutes away from becoming a synonym for technological disaster.

*   *   *

The last few minutes before the disaster were reconstructed by the Soviet investigating team largely on the

---

* The role of the International Atomic Energy Agency (IAEA) in the Chernobyl disaster is the subject of Chapter Ten. The Soviet Union submitted its report on the accident to the agency and sent a team of officials and scientists to the agency's Vienna headquarters for a five-day post-accident review meeting in August. The Soviet report and a subsequent commentary by a group of predominantly Western nuclear experts are the basic technical documents on the accident.

basis of a mathematical model using data gathered from computer print-outs and data tapes from the control room. This mathematical model provides almost all that is known about the last four minutes of the life of reactor unit No. 4.

Just after 1.19 a.m., one of the operators cut back the flow of water into the reactor. The operator had been trying to adjust the water level – first increasing it, then decreasing it – in an attempt to keep the dangerously unstable system in some sort of equilibrium. But the controls with which he was working were insensitive, so he kept getting the levels too high or too low – just like the struggles people go through to get the water temperature right in a shower. When the operator turned back the water level, steam voids in the top half of the reactor suddenly expanded, and control rods were automatically inserted in order to keep the reactor's power from going up. The operator got a print-out from the computer monitoring system which showed that there were still too many control rods out of the reactor to allow safe operation. It was a clear and unequivocal warning to shut the reactor down. There was still time to avert catastrophe. But like sleepwalkers, the plant staff stumbled blindly on past the point of no return.

Instead of shutting down the now dangerously unstable reactor, one of the operators turned off one of the few safety systems that was still operating – a switch that would have shut the reactor down when the turbogenerator lost power. The reason was to make sure that the experiment could be repeated if necessary. In previous tests, the reactor had been allowed to shut down as a part of the experimental process. But that precaution was now swept aside with the flick of a switch.

At 1.23.04, the reactor operator took the final step to disaster when he ordered the steam supply to the turbogenerator to be shut off, an essential step for conducting the experiment. With the generator running down, the cooling pumps began to lose power, so less water flowed through the reactor. The remaining water heated rapidly and huge bubbles of steam formed. Ten seconds later, the automatic control system of the reactor started to reinsert control rods to try to make up for the increase in power, but the rods were not enough to balance the huge positive void co-efficient. By 1.23.40, it became clear to the operator that the reactor was headed into danger and he pushed the AZ-5 button, which was supposed to shut the reactor down immediately. It was too late. The control rods could not move as fast as the reaction inside the core and within the next four seconds, the reactor's power shot up from about 200 thermal megawatts to about 360,000 megawatts of thermal energy, one hundred times the maximum power for which the RBMK was designed. The Chernobyl disaster had begun.

6

THE INFERNO

Burning lumps of material and sparks shot into the air above the reactor, some of which fell onto the roof of the machine room and started a fire. . . . [There was] a fireworks display of glowing particles and fragments escaping from the units.

USSR State Committee on the
Utilisation of Atomic Energy[1]

At 1.23.40 a.m. on April 26th, one of the operators at the Chernobyl nuclear power station pushed the AZ-5 button to shut down reactor No. 4. Hitting the AZ-5 is the most drastic action that an operator can take to bring a reactor under control: doing so is supposed to trigger an uncontrolled power reduction and the complete shutdown of the reactor.

The mechanism producing this shutdown is the dropping of 199 boron carbide control rods directly into the core of the reactor. When those rods fall into place, they absorb so many neutrons that a continued nuclear reaction is no longer possible.

The rods hang above the reactor, held in place by clamps that, at the touch of the AZ-5 button, release them into free fall. They drop at a speed of forty centimetres a second. It takes almost twenty seconds to insert the rods fully into the reactor core. By way of comparison, the control rods can be inserted into the CANDU reactor in approximately one second. The reason that the control rods take so long to insert into the RBMK is because they are falling into water-filled channels in which the water is flowing upwards under high pressure. The Soviet report on the accident says that both mathematical and test-bench studies were conducted of the AZ-5 emergency protection system which showed that 'the measures and systems foreseen guarantee the safety of RBMK reactors in all modes resulting from equipment failure.'[2] But on April 26th, the AZ-5 system failed its most severe test: it wasn't fast enough to save Chernobyl No. 4.

* * *

The surge of power that the AZ-5 button came too late to stop was the result of a sudden massive increase in the number of fissions taking place inside the reactor. An event that should never happen inside a nuclear reactor had taken place, something the reactor designers call, in their arcane language, 'super-prompt criticality.' What that means is that the reactor was pushed out of control because the prompt neutrons were able to drive the reaction along without the help of the delayed neutrons. With the prompt neutrons alone sufficient to drive the reaction, the slow-moving control rods were incapable of getting far enough into the reactor rapidly enough to keep the reaction from building power. This super-prompt criticality lasted only instants – until the fission energy caused the fuel in the reactor to fly apart.

It wasn't, strictly speaking, an explosion. That word has a precise technical definition. But what happened when the fuel disintegrated would have looked very much like a slow motion explosion to a layman.

The fuel in the RBMK was in the form of pellets of slightly enriched uranium dioxide. The pellets were packed in tubes of zirconium metal, each tube about eleven feet long. Each of the 1,661 fuel channels of the reactor contained thirty-six of these tubes, a total of almost 60,000 separate zirconium tubes filled with uranium. To keep these tubes cool and to draw off the heat that made the steam turbogenerators spin, water flowed around the tubes, which are called fuel elements.

The first step in the wrecking of Chernobyl reactor No. 4 was apparently the rapid disintegration of the fuel in many of the fuel elements. The immense energy of the surging chain reaction caused the pellets of extremely hot uranium to break up and spread out like shot. The sudden dispersion of the fuel was the inevitable end of the out-of-control fissions, what is known in nuclear jargon as a 'reactivity excursion.' The reactivity excursion was halted only when the fuel spread apart to such an extent that it no longer was dense enough to sustain a chain reaction. The reactivity excursion caused the complex chemical and physical reactions that took place after the fuel fragmented. Those chemical and physical reactions produced the catastrophe of Chernobyl.

* * *

The composition of everything in the RBMK reactor assembly was chosen for a reason. Graphite was chosen as the moderator because it is excellent for slowing down neutrons. In addition, it is easy to fabricate to precise shapes. But it is inflammable at extremely high temperatures. The zirconium alloy fuel element tubes were selected for the tubes of the fuel elements because zirconium doesn't absorb many neutrons. Other metals do, so they become brittle under the intense radioactive bombardment that takes place inside a reactor. Zirconium is also slow to corrode in water, even under high radiation. So long as the temperatures inside the reactor stayed where they were supposed to, the combination of zirconium alloy fuel assemblies, a graphite moderator and water was nearly ideal.[3]

When temperatures rise, however, zirconium becomes less stable. At about 1,100 degrees, it starts to react with water, producing zirconium dioxide and explosive hydrogen gas. The reaction of zirconium and water produces more heat. Other chemical changes begin to happen as temperatures rise. For instance, as zirconium heats up, it becomes a good absorber of oxygen and may start to extract oxygen from the uranium dioxide fuel pellets, producing a new liquid form of fuel that includes dissolved uranium metal. All these complex reactions can lead to a weakening of the zirconium walls of the fuel elements. And as the zirconium heats, it becomes less able to resist pressure which can build up inside the fuel tubes.

At the same time, hot zirconium that is in contact with the graphite supporting structure of the reactor can start another reaction, one that produces zirconium carbide. A byproduct of this reaction is even more heat. If the fuel tubes rupture and the uranium fuel inside comes in contact with super-hot graphite, still another reaction can take place which produces another explosive gas – carbon monoxide.

Even after lengthy analysis of the events that took place in the seconds after the AZ-5 button was hit, there is still no total consensus on just what happened once the fuel in the reactor disintegrated. What is known is this:

The control rods started down into the reactor, but before they could reach deep enough to stop the reaction, at least some of the fuel elements – apparently those in the top of the reactor – flew apart. An authoritative estimate is that about thirty per cent of the fuel disintegrated. The fuel, bursting with energy, flew into the superheated water and hot graphite around it. Big volumes of steam were suddenly produced. Fragments of hot zirconium probably reacted with the water to make hydrogen, too. The build-up in steam caused the piping of the fuel channels to rupture and particles of super-hot uranium dioxide, zirconium and graphite blasted up through the top of the reactor and right out onto the roof of the reactor hall. These ruptures were not enough to compensate for the tremendous pressures that had now built up inside the reactor. Within seconds, the pressure built to levels which the reactor core's flimsy containment structure was never designed to withstand.

What happened next was that the top plate of the reactor core, a 1,000 ton cover, was blown off the reactor, severing all the rest of the fuel channels, shearing off the partially inserted control rods and cutting the cooling water pipes that brought water into the reactor. The force of lifting of the plate was apparently great enough to dislodge a huge crane that ran across tracks in the reactor hall. When the crane fell, it knocked over the big refuelling machine that was used to remove fuel elements from the reactor and the machine fell into the burning reactor core.

Within a few more seconds, another explosion occurred. This may have been caused by another surge of radioactive release or by exploding hydrogen, released from the core when the containment chamber blew apart. The second explosion blasted uranium fuel out of the bottom of the reactor core, blew chunks of burning graphite out of the reactor and ruptured a water-filled tank that surrounded the reactor and was supposed to absorb radiation. The water from the tank flooded into the reactor core, the reactor hall and the area below the reactor. Huge quantities of radioactive steam were produced and sucked up by the power plant's ventilating system, spreading contamination into the air the plant workers were breathing, while inside the reactor, superheated zirconium, uranium, water and graphite were interacting, producing volatile gases and fuelling the release of millions of curies of radiation into the atmosphere. Chunks of burning graphite and super-hot uranium and zirconium flew out of the reactor core, landing on the roof of the reactor hall, in the generator hall and on other buildings. More than thirty separate fires broke out. In less than a minute, Chernobyl nuclear power station had turned into an inferno.

* * *

At the time of the disaster, 176 members of the staff of the station were on duty at the four operating reactors. In addition, 268 construction workers were labouring at the site where two more RBMK power units were under construction. Apparently only two of these people, a reactor operator named Valery Khodemchuk and another staff member named Vladimir Shashnok, were killed immediately. Khodemchuk's body was never recovered from the plant and Shashnok died after staggering from the fiery reactor building, muttering the name of his dead colleague.

Some of the operators who were on duty in the control room at the time of the accident rushed out to the reactor hall to see what had happened. Others stayed on at the now useless control panels. The ones who went into the hall were among the staff members to receive the heaviest doses of radiation and were among the eventual deaths from radiation sickness, according to Soviet officials. However, it appears likely that the control room itself caught fire and was heavily irradiated.[4]

In the aftermath of the explosions and fire, it took some moments for anyone to manage to make a call to the local fire department. Not until 1.30 was the message passed that there was a fire at the power plant. Three fire units from Chernobyl town and from Pripyat set out to the stricken plant. As they drove toward it, they could see in the night sky the blazing roof of the reactor building and an eerie glowing, pyrotechnic column of incandescent particles streaming up from the reactor as the heat of the burning graphite forced a bewildering and terrifying array of radioactive substances into the foggy night air.

The firemen who came on the scene were ill-prepared to deal with the catastrophe before them. They came to the task without radiation-protective clothing. One of the firemen was wearing only a short-sleeved shirt. They were hampered in reaching the fires on the roof of the reactor hall, 150 feet in the air, by the lack of hydraulic lifting equipment. But it was clear they would have to control quickly the fires that were raging because there was already a danger that the blaze on the roof of the machine hall – which was shared with reactor No. 3 –

threatened to draw the No. 3 reactor unit into the unfolding disaster.

When the Soviet news media began to tell the story of Chernobyl the heroism and self-sacrifice of these ill-equipped men figured prominently, and it is easy to see why. By the time the firemen arrived, about 600 square yards of the reactor hall were burning. The roof had been covered with flammable roofing material, apparently a substance that had already been banned for twelve years because of fires in other industrial settings, a charge contained in an officially-approved Soviet play about Chernobyl called *Sarcophagus*.[5]

Pravda reported that when the firemen managed to reach the blazing roof of the power plant:

> . . . their boots stuck in the bitumen that melted because of the high temperature; soot and smoke made it difficult to breathe, but the brave, bold men kept fighting the blaze courageously.[6]

In addition to the blazing roofs, the firemen were faced with burning hunks of graphite that had been blasted up from the reactor core. They used water, foam sprays and gas to put out the blazes. They knew that if they failed to conquer the fire, the No. 3 reactor unit was in danger, and they were aware that there was a need to save the undamaged parts of the No. 4 unit if any headway was to be made in bringing the disaster under control and containing the release of radioactivity from the reactor core. They also had to contend with other problems, such as the imminent danger that chemical and fuel stores on the power plant site would either catch fire or explode.

The firemen had to contend with another enemy besides the visible fire – radiation. According to Soviet television, the radiation field into which the firemen were thrust was so intense that the measuring devices the firemen carried went off their scales.[7] The firemen faced all sorts of radiation dangers: the air they breathed was full of tiny aerosol particles of almost every imaginable radioactive substance; the open core of the reactor was giving off high levels of both beta and gamma rays, and particles of radioactive material rained down on them, burning into their skin. It is in no way surprising that the Soviet Union honoured fire chief Major Leonid Telyatnikov and two deceased members of the fire crew, Viktor Kibenok and Vladimir Pravik, with the nation's highest decoration, the title 'Hero of the Soviet Union', for their actions in those pre-dawn hours. Nor is it surprising that when the death toll was counted, the firemen made up the biggest number of Chernobyl's early victims.

Even while the firemen were struggling to bring the fire under control, reactor operators were trying to do what they could to regain control over the shattered No. 4 reactor core.

The operators used the only resource they had left – water. In the hours after the accident they flooded the ruptured reactor unit with up to a million gallons of water. They only stopped pumping water over the shattered and highly radioactive reactor when the contaminated water threatened to flood the other massive power unit that housed the Nos. 1 and 2 reactor units. For about half a day, the operators continued to pump water in at the rate of up to eighty thousand gallons an hour. They did so despite the fact that there was a real danger that if significant quantities of water came into direct contact with the highly heated zirconium cladding of the fuel elements, the resulting chemical reaction could produce big volumes of highly explosive hydrogen gas. In retrospect, it appears that the reason this did not happen is that the explosions at the start of the accident made it impossible to pump water directly into the burning core: instead, the water appears to have poured into the well below the reactor. Some steam was observed coming from the well on the first day of the accident and it is believed that the water may have added negligible quantities of hydrogen and carbon monoxide gases to the raging reactor fire.[8]

Dr Adolf Birkhofer, a member of the IAEA international nuclear safety group and director of the West German Company for Reactor Safety (a quasi-government regulatory agency), said that using the water may have had significant benefits in containing the accident.[9] But he also said that the contaminated water, which poured out of the damaged reactor, threatened to pollute a major Ukrainian water supply. The power plant is sited on the banks of the Pripyat River, just north of its juncture with the River Uzh. Both those rivers flow into the Dnieper River which feeds the Kiev reservoir, a 370-square mile lake called the Kiev Sea, which is the main water supply for the Ukrainian capital, the third largest city of the Soviet Union, with a population of 2.5 million people. In the days immediately after the accident, one of the priority tasks was the building of cofferdams around the plant site. When the work was announced by the Soviet authorities, it was generally believed that the reason for the cofferdams was to prevent possible water pollution in the event of rain around the plant. But it now seems possible that the cofferdams were rushed to completion to try to ensure that none of the radioactive water escaped. Later, Soviet media were to criticise the decision to put the Chernobyl plant in a location where water pollution on such a major scale was a danger – though, to be fair, nearly all nuclear power plants are in fact located near major water sources.

* * *

The reactor operators who were struggling to control the reactor core which their actions had blown apart can scarcely have been in much doubt about the seriousness of the situation in which they found themselves. But there is evidence that others in the immediate area of the Chernobyl plant had no idea of just how deadly dangerous the accident was, at least at first. Western intelligence sources believe that as many as 200 people from Pripyat drove out in their cars in the early hours of April 26th to watch the fire and the spectacular eruptions from the crippled reactor. Though Pripyat was a town built around the nuclear industry, many people were apparently ignorant of the dangers of radioactivity. But they were not alone in their ignorance. American satellite pictures of the Chernobyl area soon after the disaster showed the wrecked reactor with its roof blown out; the same pictures showed a barge sailing peacefully down the Pripyat River as if nothing had happened and, inside the plant fence, less than a mile from the wrecked reactor, a group of men apparently playing soccer.

One reason that there may have been a certain obliviousness to the danger is suggested by the play *Sarcophagus*: in one scene, the man in charge of taking radiation readings at the plant tells legal officials that the equipment he used was thirty years old, had come from a warehouse after being repeatedly repaired and that the responsible officials refused requests for replacements. But the play may well have exaggerated its claims on the decrepitude of the equipment.

Whatever the reason, there was a total collapse of the radiation monitoring system for Chernobyl No. 4 because, according to the IAEA safety group's report:

. . . the regular [radiation] measurement systems in the plant had broken down completely. The outputs of detectors which might have survived were inaccessible to the plant personnel because of the radiation field.[10]

But within a few hours, 'pretty high quality radiation monitoring was taking place' at the site, according to one Western expert who discussed the accident in detail with Soviet nuclear experts.[11] If that is true, it only increases puzzlement about the motives of the plant authorities for failing to order an immediate shut-down of the other reactors at the power plant in the aftermath of the accident.

The No. 3 reactor, which shared some common facilities with the destroyed No. 4 unit, was kept running for more than three and a half hours after the explosions ripped its twin reactor apart, during the whole time in which fire threatened to engulf the machine room and possibly spread to the control room of the No. 3 reactor. Even more surprising was the revelation that the Nos. 1 and 2 reactor units continued to operate for more than 24 hours after the disaster began. According to the Soviet report on the accident, it was not until 2.13 a.m. on April 27th that all units at the Chernobyl nuclear power station ceased operation.

The Soviet report on the accident makes it clear that economic considerations play a major role in safety decisions. In a description of the emergency protection system, the report notes:

> In view of the large contribution of nuclear power plants with the RBMK reactors to the general power grid, it is necessary to reduce to a minimum the outages of such plants. . . .[12]

The haste with which the authorities moved to put the Chernobyl plant back into operation after the accident – with at least one unit producing electricity within only six months of the accident – shows just how important the plant is to the economy of the region. The Chernobyl plant represented a major investment. An instantaneous shut-down of a reactor – what reactor operators call a 'trip' or a 'scram' – puts real stresses on components of the system, stresses than can lead to costly and time-consuming maintenance. So it seems possible that the decision to take more time to shut down the other units was based at least partly on a desire to protect the investment.

Did the decision not to shut down and to keep the other units operating lead to more injuries? About 300 on-site personnel had to be sent to hospitals for radiation injuries and burns.[13] There are indications that at least some of these personnel were workers who remained to operate the other units instead of being evacuated: the report of the

Western nuclear experts who debriefed the Soviet team in Vienna hints at this with its recommendation that in view of the Chernobyl experience:

> Future [research] work should discuss the design criteria and the effects of ventilation in the early phases after the accident and the consequences for occupational radiation and habitability of control rooms and vital parts of the installations, considering also the case of stations with multiple units on the same site.[14]

*   *   *

While the full extent of the accident may not have been immediately apparent, Western intelligence sources claim that the top Soviet leadership was alerted to the fact that a severe accident had taken place in Chernobyl well before daybreak of April 26th.

One of the first high-ranking officials on the scene was a Ukrainian deputy interior minister, Gennadiy V. Berdov, who arrived at Chernobyl as dawn was breaking from his home in Kiev.[15] Later in the day, a high-ranking scientific delegation from the Atomic Energy Institute in Moscow arrived. Academician Valery Legasov, who would direct the technical work to control the reactor disaster and lead the Soviet team that reported on the accident to the International Atomic Energy Agency, was in charge.[16]

The scientific delegation was followed by a government commission headed by the country's top trouble-shooter, Deputy Prime Minister Boris Shcherbina, who had made a name for himself by his efforts to deal with oil production problems in Siberia. Shcherbina arrived in Chernobyl on the day after the disaster and took charge energetically: later he was to complain at a news conference in Moscow that local officials had underestimated the scope of the disaster. After spending ten days organising the initial effort, Shcherbina was replaced as leader of the commission staff in Chernobyl by another deputy prime minister,

Lev Voronin. In the weeks to come, a series of deputy prime ministers rotated in the Chernobyl post, apparently out of concern for possible long-term health dangers they might face.

But even before Shcherbina arrived, someone had taken a crucial decision: the reactor would have to be smothered in order to bring it under control. And in order to get close enough to do that, aerial bombardment was the only feasible method. An order went out for helicopters.

One of the pilots, Air Force Major-General Nikolai Antoshchkin told how on the evening of April 26th he had received an order by telephone: 'Leave urgently for the town of Pripyat. They have decided to smother the accident-stricken block there with sand . . . obviously no other technique besides helicopters can work.' On his arrival he was told by Shcherbina: 'Everything depends on you and your helicopter pilots.'

The helicopters dumped 5,000 tons of sand, lead, clay, dolomite and boron carbide onto the reactor. Boron carbide was to absorb neutrons, the lead was to shield against gamma radiation, to absorb heat and to form an airtight cap over the reactor, and the clay, sand and dolomite were to absorb fission products and to bind the materials together.

Local truck drivers were put to work digging clay in the village of Chistogalovka, little more than two miles from the plant. They worked from April 28th until they had to be sent to hospitals for radiation sickness on May 2nd.[17]

On the first day, the helicopters flew ninety-three sorties, on the second 186. On the first flights, the helicopters carried a single sack which was pushed out of the cargo door by hand, each run adding so little material that Shcherbina compared it to a hunter taking 'small shot to an elephant.' But later they dropped six to eight sacks at a time from nets slung below the fuselage. When it was found that the airdrops had covered the reactor thinly, the pilots were sent back to lower sand bags by rope and to dump fine lead shot to fill in the cracks. Air traffic controllers were brought in to direct the operations: ground controllers gave the orders while a small plane flew alongside to monitor the operation.

Particularly in the first few days radiation levels were high, and the pilots could spend only a few seconds over the gaping roof of the reactor. The Soviet fliers wore special protective clothing, but it was only on later flights that the helicopters were fitted with protective lead shielding. The crews were at risk because the gaseous and aerosol products spewing from the reactor were potentially lethal. They flew directly into plumes of caesium, iodine, strontium, tellurium, neptunium and other highly dangerous radioactive substances including plutonium.

The decision to bombard the reactor appears in retrospect to have been a good one, though there were major doubts about it at the time. For one thing, no one was sure that the reactor's supports could take the weight of the material – there was the possibility that the tons of minerals would send the reactor crashing down into the vault below, perhaps even into a huge tank of water that had been built into the unit as a safety device. Had that happened, there is every likelihood that the result would have been massive steam explosions and a further spread of radioactivity. Another fear was that blanketing the reactor would trap so much heat inside it that a full core meltdown – the 'China Syndrome' – could result. The China Syndrome, in which a mass of molten uranium eats its way into the heart of the earth, has been discounted by many Western nuclear experts. They point out that the uranium would not only burn down, but would also spread out, eventually diluting itself. But there are real worries about what would happen if a sufficient mass of hot reactor fuel burned its way out of the reactor core and came into contact with the concrete that makes up the structure of nuclear power plants.

In a private conversation on the subject, one acknowledged international expert explained that it is difficult to say just what would have happened if a molten mass of uranium started to attack the concrete of the reactor building since detailed knowledge of both the state of the core debris and the type of concrete used in constructing the building are lacking. The chemistry depends on whether the concrete has been made from silaceous rock, like granite, or a carbonate, like limestone. The interaction of molten fuel and either type of concrete produces steam, which can then react to produce explosive hydrogen gas. Silaceous concrete melts at a lower temperature than does limestone-based concrete but limestone concrete can react with molten fuel to produce explosive carbon monoxide gas. Nobody has yet determined which sort of concrete is safer for reactor construction.

There were two options: to allow the fire in the reactor to burn itself out, or to attempt to contain the accident by covering the reactor with heat absorbent material. The first alternative was quickly ruled out since it carried the risk of further large releases of radioactivity, and the nightmare of high levels of nuclear fallout on the cities of Kiev and Minsk, with their combined population of about four million people. Sealing off the reactor was the only real choice.

By the time the pilots started to arrive with their machines, the level of releases from the reactor core was substantially down from the initial level. In the first day of the accident, about twenty-five per cent of the total radioactivity that came from Chernobyl was released. Over the next six days, the release rate declined to a minimum value of about six times lower than the initial rate, though still significant enough to pose a major public health hazard. By April 30th, the reactor control operation looked like a success. Releases were down, and, nearly as important, the temperatures inside the reactor were falling, a sign that the graphite fires were burning out and that there was no chain reaction.

But on May Day, the picture started to change, with the discharges from the reactor starting to increase again. By the next day, the reactor was showing signs of reheating. On May 3rd, the decision was taken to suspend the dropping of material on the reactor from helicopters. Over the four days from May 1st to the 5th, the reactor increased emissions until it was putting out about seventy per cent as much radioactive pollution as it had on the first day of the accident. What had happened?

The Soviet scientists who reported on the accident and the international experts who studied their report and questioned them admit they don't know. In the dry words of the international safety group's report:

> Perhaps the most unusual feature of the release [of radioactivity] is its increasing rate beginning about six days after the accident. *No definitive explanation for this has been offered.* (authors' emphasis)[18]

Among the possible reasons that have been suggested for the rising temperature and discharges were:

– that more gases were generated inside the reactor which produced new chemical reactions.

– that 'some unidentified mechanism' caused more burning inside the reactor.

– that the material dumped on the reactor had at first absorbed heat but later was unable to absorb any more.

Another suggestion was that the zirconium metal of the fuel cladding and the uranium fuel started to react.

If this were the case, the reactor core must have been extremely hot, because the zirconium-uranium reaction only takes place at temperatures above 1,500 degrees. But what happened inside the reactor to cause the reheating remains, for now, one of Chernobyl's mysteries.

The sharp increase in radiation and heat was not the last of the mysteries: just as the reactor appeared to be headed totally out of control once again, on May 5th, the releases and the heating abruptly stopped. Why?

The international safety experts have provided several suggestions.

The first is that the increased radiation was caused by the increased heat in the reactor after May 1st. The heat would not only have increased radiation but might actually have raised temperatures to the point that the debris of the core melted and dripped down into the ruptured cooling water pipes under the reactor, where it solidified again, helped to cool by the nitrogen gas that the reactor control team had started pumping into the base of the building.

Second, it is suggested that the capping of the reactor may itself have stifled the fire inside. It has also been pointed out that around May 5th, the reactor core was being bathed with nitrogen, which might have had the effect of both lowering the temperature and smothering fire. Also, around that time, the core subsided to some extent. But the experts admit that this is all guesswork: they still do not know for certain what caused the reactor to stop erupting.

*   *   *

In the first few days, the strain on the nuclear technicians who manned the control rooms of the three shut-down reactors was immense. But like the firemen and helicopter pilots, they displayed heroism. *Radio Moscow* quoted one worker as saying he had worked four days and nights without sleep, although it was not clear how much of that time he had spent at the plant. Martin Walker, Moscow correspondent of the *Guardian* newspaper, said Soviet scientists told him that nuclear technicians were flown to Chernobyl from around the Soviet Union to keep the control rooms manned on a rotation basis, taking it in turns to go into the radiation-soaked areas for a few hours at a time. But there was fear at one stage that the Soviet Union might run out of nuclear technicians prepared to risk their lives in the contaminated plant.

Also working in the exclusion zone were military personnel and police who were coordinating the emergency measures around the plant. Police in gas masks directed military trucks at intersections devoid of civilian cars. Workers hosed radioactive dust off trees and buildings. Soviet television film showed later that some were dressed in street clothes: it was a measure of the inadequacies of the Soviet civil defence system. Truck drivers carrying the building materials and other equipment to the plant to fight the disaster had to travel on a route that took them through the village of Kopachi only a mile away from the wrecked reactor, exposing them to heavy doses of radiation. Initially, a decision was taken to have the vehicles take a short cut across open country, but their wheels stirred up too much radioactive dust. Eventually, the problem was solved when the commission called for volunteers to build a new one-mile highway. The workers worked shifts of only two hours and were allowed to work only six in every twenty-four hours.

There were many tales of individual heroism among the thousands of scientists, technicians, construction workers and soldiers who came to Chernobyl. Indeed, Soviet press reporting presented the struggle to contain the accident in military terms, speaking of the Chernobyl campaign and harking back to the days of the Second World War. But, just as in war, not everyone was a hero: in the moments after the operators at reactor No. 4 made the decision to push the AZ-5 button in the early hours of April 26th, some plant workers, including foremen of shifts and senior technicians, fled into the night, according to Soviet press accounts. Some were still on the run weeks later. *Pravda*, while extolling the heroism of other relief workers, referred to this 'panic-stricken' exodus. *Pravda* also reported that in the 'tight corners revealed by the accident,' some officials turned out to be 'psychologically unready.' The Kiev regional Communist Party leader, Grigori Revenko, told the newspaper *Sovietskaya Rossiya* on May 7th that 'individual workers were found who in difficult conditions did not display the necessary will and steadfastness to be in the front line'. A number of workers were disciplined for deserting their posts or for dereliction of duty to subordinates.

*   *   *

During the first days of the accident, no one was sure just what would be needed to control the disaster. The possibility that the fuel in the reactor would melt through the bottom of the core and down into the lower depths of the building and into the ground was at the forefront of the list of worries.

The first fear was that there might be a massive hydrogen explosion if molten fuel ate its way through to a huge tank of water in the base of the reactor. The pool – a pressure suppression pool designed to cool and absorb possible overpressure from the reactor – obviously had to be drained. But this was an incredibly dangerous job.

A team of divers was sent into the damaged plant and made their way down to the level above the pool. They were being bombarded with high-level radioactivity and had to find their way in the dark. But eventually they managed to enter the pool and then find the valve that had to be opened to drain away the water. Even when the pool was drained, there was still fear that the fuel might reach the foundation and eat its way into the ground, where it would contaminate the groundwater.

Almost immediately after the accident, a plan was hatched to tunnel around the reactor and inject the ground with liquid nitrogen in order to freeze it, thus making sure that possible contamination would not spread. A team of subway constructors from Kiev and Moscow was brought in and began to dig shafts toward the reactor. Because of the high levels of radiation they encountered, they could dig for only four hours at a time.[19] This plan to inject the ground with nitrogen was to supplement the pumping of nitrogen into the spaces beneath the reactor itself.

When the reactor began to cool down, the nitrogen injection plan was abandoned and the subway builders were sent home. In their place, a team of coal miners from the Donets Basin and from near Moscow was assembled: their job was to dig another tunnel, this one *under* the reactor. The coal miners, like the subway constructors, had to work in conditions of intense radiation: their shifts were limited to three hours. The job before them was to dig tunnels big enough for mine cars to haul concrete under the reactor to build a new foundation. The new foundation was thought necessary to shore up the existing underpinnings of the unit, which might have given way. A special feature of the foundation was to be the incorporation of heat exchangers which would draw off heat from the reactor. About 380 miners worked on the project from some time in May until June 24th, when the project was reported to have been completed.[20] One Western expert on reactor accidents said that the decision to put concrete under the reactor was a good one – the effect, he said, was like putting an ice cube in a drink, since the concrete acted as a giant heat sink.

Shoring up the foundation was one thing. Doing something about the exposed reactor was another, even more complicated task. There weren't any viable alternatives.

Getting rid of a nuclear power plant is difficult, even under the best of conditions. The problems involved in taking apart a huge structure, much of it heavily irradiated, and disposing of it in a safe manner are myriad, so much so that some opponents of nuclear power say that when the time comes to start decommissioning the current generation of nuclear plants, the costs will be so high that nuclear power will no longer seem like a bargain.

But it is relatively simple to decommission a plant that has been shut down properly and which has had its nuclear fuel removed. At Chernobyl, where the walls, ceiling and roof of the reactor hall were covered with radioactive elements, where the reactor fuel was strewn about inside the reactor core and in the pipes below, where the entire environment was irradiated, the problem was colossal. It soon became apparent to the scientists and officials who were attempting to cope with the accident that they could not expect to dismantle Chernobyl No. 4. Instead, they decided to entomb it.

Nothing like this had ever been tried before: in the words of the international safety group, the entombment would be 'a major technical innovation which will be of great interest to experts throughout the nuclear safety community.'[21]

The Chernobyl power plant is almost half a mile long, from one end of unit No. 1 to the far end of unit No. 4. Before the accident, it was a mass of rectangles. Now, what has been built at one end resembles a sort of Mexican step-pyramid, a nuclear-age burial vault.

The top of the pyramid rises about 180 feet in the air, a gently sloping cover over the demolished reactor hall. The stair-steps that march up the side of the building cover piles of radioactive rubble. A sloping incline runs from the roof of the reactor hall down to the lower level of the turbine room. Buttresses support the new concrete protective walls that are meant to block the radiation from the core. Inside the turbine hall, a metal partition wall blocks off the two now-stilled turbogenerators of unit No. 4 from the turbines for the No. 3 unit.

Deep inside the reactor building, concrete has been poured over the debris of the emergency core cooling system and over the main cooling water pumps. Throughout the summer, thousands of workers laboured to build the tomb for unit No. 4 and by late September, Shcherbina was able to announce in Vienna that the tomb was, for all practical purposes, complete. Now, he said, Chernobyl was safe for the work of bringing the remaining three generating units back to life. He joked that it would be possible to run tourist excursions to the site.

Months later, the newspaper *Sotsialisticheskaya Indus-triya* carried a story announcing that only in late November had the entombment actually been completed. And a British nuclear industry trade union delegation who visited the Soviet Union in November was not taken to the plant site, despite Shcherbina's jest about making the locale into a tourist site.

Still, there was no question that the tomb was a major feat of engineering. But unanswered questions hung in the air. The main question was: how long could the tomb last? Soviet officials had spoken of the entombment as a permanent solution to the problem, but the international safety experts were not so sure. They were worried that the vast weight of concrete that had been poured on the site might crack the reactor's foundations and open the way for groundwater pollution. They said they were concerned about the way the tomb would be ventilated. The design adopted for the tomb includes an active ventilation system: if the ventilation machinery should fail, there is a danger that explosive hydrogen gas could accumulate inside the tomb. Most important, they were worried about the ability of the concrete to withstand the heat that the entombed nuclear debris will continue to radiate for years.

During discussions with the international experts, Soviet scientists revealed that they, too, were worried about this problem. They had undertaken studies using a type of concrete which is supposed to melt only at temperatures of 2,000 degrees. But the Soviets acknowledged that using the concrete in this application was experimental and that it was difficult to work with. That was one problem. But there was another.

The international experts said that after fifty years or so, the reliability of the tomb as a containment for the radiation would begin to suffer. A *Pravda* report on the project said the reactor could be entombed 'for centuries' but Soviet scientists have apparently acknowledged privately that the tomb will have to undergo continuing maintenance in order to protect the environment until Chernobyl unit No. 4 is no longer dangerous. How long will that be?

Fissile plutonium has a half-life of 24,400 years. Uranium^{235} has a somewhat longer decay period: its half life is 4.5 million years.

7

THE DRAGON'S TAIL

Cancer in individuals down the line – ten, twenty or thirty years from now – will not have a little flag on it which pops up and says: 'I was caused by Chernobyl.'

John Gofman, Professor Emeritus of Medical Physics at the University of California, Berkeley[1]

A brilliant young Canadian physicist, Louis Slotin, who helped pioneer the US atomic bomb, used to flirt with death when testing the interior mechanisms of the experimental bombs. The interiors of the weapons consisted of two hemispheres of uranium which when driven together would produce an atomic blast. But the physics of nuclear weapons was still experimental, and many calculations could only be made on the basis of experience. Slotin was one of the experimenters who helped to gather that data. Slotin was in the habit of experimenting without taking any protective precautions, using two screwdrivers to slide the two hemispheres towards each other on a rod, while he watched them with intense concentration. His object was to do no more than just reach the critical point, the very first stage in the chain reaction, which would immediately stop at the moment he separated the spheres again. If he passed the point, or if he was not swift enough in breaking contact, he knew that the mass might become super critical and trigger a flash of radioactivity.

Ever since his youth, Slotin had gone in search of wars, excitement and adventure. He had volunteered for service in the Spanish Civil War, and had fought as an anti-aircraft gunner. In the Second World War, he joined the Royal Air Force but was forced to resign because of poor eyesight. He knew his experiment with the uranium hemispheres was immensely dangerous. But he derived a thrill out of risking his life in this way. He called it 'twisting the dragon's tail.' Robert Jungk, in a personal story of the early atomic scientists, told the story of what happened to Slotin:

On May 21st, 1946 . . . Slotin was carrying out an experiment, similar to those he had so often successfully performed in the past. It was connected with the preparations of the second atom-bomb test, to be performed in the waters of the South Sea atoll of Bikini. Suddenly his screwdriver slipped. The hemispheres came too close together and the material became critical. The whole room was instantly filled with a dazzling, bluish glare. Slotin, instead of ducking and thereby possibly saving himself, tore the two hemispheres apart with his hands and thus interrupted the chain reaction. By this action he saved the lives of the seven other persons in the room. He realised at once that he himself would be bound to succumb to the effects of the excessive radiation dose which he had absorbed. But he did not lose his self-control for a moment. He told his colleagues to go and stand exactly where they had been at the instant of the disaster. He then drew on the blackboard with his own hand an accurate sketch of their relative positions so that doctors could ascertain the degree of radiation to which each of those present had been exposed.

As he was sitting with Al Graves, the scientist who, except himself, had been mostly severely infected by the radiation, waiting at the roadside for the car which had been ordered to take them to the hospital, he said quietly to his companion: 'You'll come through all right. But I haven't the faintest chance myself.' It was only too true. Nine days later the man who had experimentally determined the critical mass of the first atom bomb died in terrible agony.[2]

Slotin was one of many scientists who lost his life in man's quest to understand radiation and to harness its awesome power. One of the earliest victims was the Polish-born French chemist, Marie Curie, who coined the term 'radioactivity' in 1898. She died in 1934 from a blood disease, aplastic anaemia, that was almost certainly initiated by her experiments. Her daughter, Irene, also died of aplastic anaemia. To this day Curie's notebooks remain locked in a vault in Paris, too dangerous to handle. The discoverer of the X-ray, the German physicist W. K. Roentgen, died of bone cancer in 1923. An assistant of Thomas Edison, Clarence Dally, was so seriously injured by experiments with X-rays that his hair dropped out and ulcers developed on his head, arms and hands. They turned cancerous and he died. There are many stories of early radiologists who had to have fingers or arms amputated. It is estimated that some 336 of the early radiation workers died as a result of doses they received. The story of man's experiments with radiation is one of ignorance of its dangers and of carelessness in handling radioactive materials. It was not until 1906 that it was realised that radiation could damage health.

What is radiation? How does it affect human health? Radiation is the emission and propagation of energy through space or tissue in the form of waves. Radiation exists naturally in the environment. Cosmic rays from space, granite rocks and radioactive isotopes in the soil all emit radiation, an inescapable background to which we are all exposed. Almost half the background radiation comes from cosmic rays, high energy radiation from outer space. The intensity of cosmic radiation doubles with each 5,000 feet above sea level. Inhabitants of Mexico City (7,350 feet) get a higher dose than people at sea level. As for radiation from granite rock, the annual dose in the granite city of Aberdeen is higher than in London. In New York, the radiation level is higher in Manhattan, which is built on granite, than in Brooklyn, where the soil is sandy. Though we are all exposed to it continuously, this background radiation has only a small effect on human health. Radiation unleashed by man presents the problem. It is released when uranium or plutonium atoms are split apart.[3]

Some of nature's strongest forces are locked up in the nucleus at the heart of an atom (hence the term nuclear). Atoms are made up of particles – electrons, protons and neutrons. These particles exist in a precise balance, and as long as the balance is not disrupted, nuclear forces provide a 'container' strong enough to hold the atom together. But in a nuclear power reactor, or nuclear explosion, the nuclei of atoms split open. When the atoms split, or fission, some of the mass of the atomic particles is converted to energy. The energy propels out of the atom high-speed particles and high-frequency electromagnetic waves – that is, radiation.

The body cannot feel, sense or see radiation. But it poses great health hazards. Three kinds of radiation are of prime importance: high-energy lightwaves called gamma rays, beta particles and alpha particles. The three have different energies and penetrating power and affect the body in different ways. Alpha particles, being relatively large, cannot usually penetrate the skin; even a sheet of paper is enough to stop them. But if material emitting alpha particles is inhaled, swallowed or penetrates broken skin, the alpha particles can be very damaging. Beta particles can penetrate about half an inch into the skin and human tissues, but are not usually damaging to internal organs unless beta emitting material is swallowed or inhaled. Gamma rays are very penetrating and can pass through the body. They can even penetrate aluminium, thin shields of lead and concrete. Hence their name: penetrating radiation.

There is no immediate visible physical damage when someone absorbs radiation unless the dose is enormously high. What happens is that the radiation acts on the body like a microscopic rifle. The radiation shoots electrons off the normal atoms that make up the cells of the body. This seriously disrupts the chemistry of the cell and can kill or permanently change it. The altered cells can grow out of control and turn cancerous.

The effect of radiation on the body depends on the dose – that is, the amount of radioactive energy deposited in living tissues. Radiobiologists have developed a whole set of terms to describe these amounts. The terminology can be confusing. But in the nuclear age, the measurements the terms describe can become a matter of life and death.

The amount of energy absorbed per gram of living tissue is called the absorbed dose and is measured in *rads*. The rad measures a radiation dose in terms of its physical effect. But to assess the biological effects of radiation on the human body, a modified unit, known as the *rem*, is more useful. (Rem stands for 'roentgen equivalent man,' and is named after the German physicist, Roentgen.) Rems take account of the fact that some kinds of radiation are more damaging to the body than others. Exposure to radiation is often expressed in *millirems*, or thousandths of a rem. Radiobiologists have also come up with new units, the *gray* and the *sievert*, to measure radiation doses. One gray equals 100 rads, and one sievert is equal to 100 rems. Often sieverts are expressed with the prefix, *milli* – that is, one-thousandth.

Splitting uranium atoms releases neutrons which can penetrate the human body. They are among the most biologically destructive products of the nuclear reaction. But they have a short range and can quickly be absorbed by non-radioactive materials. Neutrons, like gamma rays, are penetrating radiation.

More than 1,000 different isotopes of about ninety elements are created in a nuclear reactor. Many of them are radioactive. Some of these isotopes are so unstable that they disappear virtually within a few seconds, minutes or hours of their formation. But some persist in the environment for months or many years. The rate at which these isotopes decay is called their half-life, a term that refers to the time required for a half of a quantity of radioactive material to spontaneously disintegrate. (One thousand atoms of any element, after one half-life, reduce to 500, after another half-life 250, after another 125, and so on.) Two of the most dangerous isotopes released from the wrecked reactor at Chernobyl, iodine[131] and caesium[137], have half-lives of eight days and thirty years respectively.

What makes some of these radioisotopes particularly dangerous is that they are similar to chemicals that plants and animals – including humans – need to sustain life. That means that they can be taken up in living tissue just like non-radioactive elements. For instance, bones are vulnerable to strontium[90] which is so similar to calcium that it lodges in them where it irradiates surrounding cells for a lifetime. Caesium[137] builds up in muscles. Radioactive iodine[131] targets the thyroid gland in the neck. Some radioisotopes, like iodine, are eliminated from the body fairly quickly, but others persist for years.

Some people are more susceptible to damage from radiation than others. Particularly vulnerable are pregnant women. Radiation can damage foetuses and embryos, young children, the elderly or those chronically ill. The age at the time of irradiation is crucially important. If pregnant women are irradiated in the period from eight to about fifteen weeks after conception, there is a risk their children will suffer severe mental retardation or show diminished mental performance. But even two people of the same age, sex and general physical characteristics may respond differently to the same amount of radiation.

The health consequences of exposure to radiation fall into two categories: short-term and long-term. Exposure to large doses of radiation causes radiation sickness within minutes, hours or days. Penetrating radiation doses of 1,000 or more rads cause immediate brain damage and paralysis of the central nervous system.[4] Those exposed to somewhat lower levels of radiation are likely to die from gastrointestinal damage in the week or two following exposure. The symptoms of exposure to high doses of radiation include nausea, vomiting, intestinal cramps, fevers and severe headaches.

Other people exposed to high radiation doses – say, about 400 rems – may well not suffer at all for the first few days after the dose. But they are likely to die from massive systemic infection because radiation destroys the bone marrow which supports the body's immune systems. Infections begin in the mouth and gut. Sores around the mouth are a symptom of radiation sickness. If the bone marrow has been destroyed, the body can no longer manufacture vital blood components, like platelets, the cells which make blood clot. So, just like haemophiliacs, people with irradiated bone marrow can bleed to death. Victims of acute radiation sickness who survive for a month or so after exposure are likely not to die from these sorts of short-term effects. But for the rest of their lives, they have a much higher chance of contracting cancer of some sort.

Until now, most of what is known about acute radiation sickness came from studies of the victims of nuclear weapons. Studies of Japanese victims of radiation from the Hiroshima atomic bomb showed that people who received more than 1,000 rems of gamma radiation died within a week. Most who received 700 rems died within two months. In the range around 300 rems about half the victims, although falling seriously ill with radiation sickness, survived. Those who received doses below 200 rems survived the short-term effects of exposure.[5]

The long-term effect of exposure to radiation, even tiny doses, is a heightened risk of contracting cancer. Leukaemia begins appearing within two to five years. Later, there will be an increase in all the solid tumours – including breast, lung, gut, intestine, liver and bone cancers. The cancers begin appearing within a few years but may not develop for as long as thirty to forty years after the exposure to radiation. This means that without careful study, it is difficult to distinguish radiation-induced cancers from those caused by other factors. And since cancer is such a common disease – one in three people get it

and between one in four and five die of it – making
the link between exposure to radiation and cancer is
hard.

But there is evidence. Years of study of the survivors
of the US atomic bombs at Hiroshima and Nagasaki
gave scientists an idea of the long-term consequences of
exposure to radiation. Among the survivors were 24,000
people who received an average dose of about 130 rems.
They have since suffered over one hundred cancer deaths
more than would be usual in a population this size. Long-
term consequences of exposure to radiation may also
include a heightened probability of genetic effects, though
they may not appear until many years later. The genetic
effects may occur in the children or grandchildren of people
who absorbed very large doses, or may not emerge for
generations. Severity may range from death in childhood to
the onset of many hereditary conditions later in life. But the
evidence that radiation causes genetic damage is fairly thin:
the children of the survivors of the Hiroshima and Nagasaki
bombings have not shown any genetic effects, although it
may be that it will take two generations for genetic effects
to appear.

Proof of the long-term hazards of radiation has also come
from examining the death rates among women employed
early in the century to paint radium on luminous watch dials
and underground miners exposed to the radioactive gas
radon, which seeps out of some kinds of soil and rock. Both
these groups had higher than expected death rates. The
treatment of certain medical conditions with heavy doses of
X-rays before the radiation hazards were fully understood
also produced higher than normal cancer rates among the
patients. In Britain, about 14,000 people were dosed with
nearly 400 rems of X-rays each for treatment of rheumatoid
arthritis of the spine (a condition known as ankylosing
spondylitis). Their health has been monitored for the past
thirty years and so far they have suffered over one hundred
more cancer deaths than would be expected in a group this
size. Treatment in Germany of almost 1,000 people with

radium, also for arthritis of the spine, led to about fifty cancer deaths more than would be usual.

The explosion of the American atom bombs at Hiroshima and Nagasaki provided scientists with a unique opportunity to study the devastating consequences of exposure to radiation and the effects of radiation sickness. Now, the accident at Chernobyl will also provide unique opportunities for study and research.

* * *

City Hospital No. 6 is a nine-storey brown-brick building on the north-west outskirts of Moscow. It is the Soviet Union's leading centre for the treatment of leukaemia, aplastic anaemia and other blood disorders. After the No. 4 reactor blew apart, part of the 1,000-bed hospital was emptied and given over to 299 radiation victims. They were air-lifted from the Ukraine. Most were the reactor workers, firemen, security guards, paramedics and doctors who fought to bring the blazing reactor under control and to cope with the accident. Some had experienced vomiting and headaches within half an hour of being exposed to radiation at the plant. May Day at Hospital No. 6 was traumatic.[6]

Many of the victims had inhaled radioactive smoke and fumes containing radioactive substances. Two had extensive burns. Most of the victims had been externally irradiated with gamma and beta rays. The victims had been exposed to doses of radiation from 200 to 1,200 rads.[7] Some of the thirty-five most severely irradiated patients taken to Moscow were so sick it was immediately clear to doctors that they would die. A few had inhaled or swallowed such a large amount of radioactive material that they were radioactive themselves and presented a potential danger to the doctors and nurses around them. Others had blistering sores where radioactive particles had touched their skin; some were nauseated, many lost their hair. As the days wore on, the patients developed stomach and intestinal problems, jaundice and fevers. Some fell into comas. Their bodies contained a mixture of nuclides, mainly isotopes of iodine, caesium, zirconium, niobium and ruthenium. Tests showed that the thyroid glands of the victims were contaminated with iodine[131].

Beta radiation from radioactive particles that had settled on their skin and clothes caused severe skin burns in forty-eight of the victims. In some cases, beta burns covered up to ninety per cent of the victims' bodies. The burns, which proved difficult to treat, contributed greatly to the deaths of some of the patients. Treatment was even more complicated because the patients had also suffered gamma radiation.

One way to treat patients who have been severely irradiated is with bone marrow transplants, and an American bone marrow transplant surgeon, Dr Robert Gale, offered to assist the Soviet Union. Gale, a controversial figure, was renowned for running an international network of bone marrow transplant centres. However, he was rebuked in 1985 by the US National Institutes of Health for performing certain transplants without first receiving approval from hospital authorities.

Gale made contact with Moscow through Dr Armand Hammer, the veteran American industrialist who over the years had built up a unique personal and business relationship with the Soviet Union, a relationship that dated back to 1921 when Hammer arranged grain shipments to the Soviet Union during a famine and typhus epidemic. Hammer, chairman of Occidental Petroleum, wrote a letter that was cabled by the Soviet Embassy in Washington to General Secretary Mikhail Gorbachev. Hammer outlined Gale's offer to help and said he would 'bear all costs for his efforts.' On April 30th, Moscow politely declined an offer of official assistance from the United States. But on May Day, the acting Soviet Ambassador in Washington, Oleg Sokolov, telephoned Gale to invite him to Moscow.

Gale arrived at the hospital at 23 Marshal Novikov Street quickly. Nothing in his experience prepared him for what he found. So many patients required urgent treatment that the Soviet doctors and Gale resorted to battlefield triage – separating those with the best chance of survival from those most likely to die. Gale said later: 'Doctors spend huge amounts of time, professionally and socially, discussing what would happen if someone dropped a bomb or a nuclear submarine radiated its crew, and here was I, awe-struck, face to face with people who'd been accidentally irradiated.' He was joined in Moscow by two other American doctors and an Israeli biophysicist. The Americans, both from UCLA, were Dr Richard Champlin, an expert in post-operative care, and Dr Paul Terasaki, an immunologist. They were joined by Dr Yair Reisner, a biophysicist from Israel's Weizmann Institute of Science.

Because some of their patients were radioactive, their urine, blood, stools and secretions had to be handled with care. To visit them the Soviet and American doctors changed into masks, uniforms and shoe covers. The patients were in a sterile area of the hospital. The medical teams entered and left this area through ante-rooms with plastic-lined walls. On the way out, the doctors checked themselves with geiger counters. Once Champlin's shoe registered radiation. He wiped it off on a floor mat.

Champlin later gave a grim account of the state of the radiation victims.[8] Both he and Gale were used to seeing people who had received relatively high doses of controlled radiation, but they had never seen patients in this state before. Champlin said two patients stood out in his memory.

One man, in his mid-twenties, had been among the first inside the plant. His injuries were among the worst. He had suffered extreme radiation damage to his intestine and it was clear he would not live. What Champlin found inexplicable about this patient's fate was that in the adjacent room lay another fireman, who had fought the blaze from a position perhaps twenty feet away. Those twenty feet were the margin of life and death, for the second man would survive. His injuries were much less severe. Champlin said that the young fireman knew he had received a fatal dose yet he was not terrified. He had the same stoic look of many of Champlin's leukaemia patients in the United States. The man died early one morning. When Champlin arrived to make his rounds, the man's wife was weeping outside his door. She was comforted by nurses.

The other patient Champlin remembered was a Soviet doctor in his thirties who had lived near Chernobyl. He was introduced as a hero because, knowing the risks, he had gone into the nuclear reactor building in an attempt to rescue people injured in the explosion. When Champlin met him, he was still conscious although intermittently delirious. His injuries were the worst of all the patients, and his suffering grew every day. In his mouth and on his face were large black herpes simplex blisters. His skin literally broke down. First the folds around the groin and under the armpits became red and ulcerated. Slowly these ulcers spread across his entire body. Within a few days, he was covered with weeping skin burns. By the end he was barely recognisable. The doctors administered morphine, constantly stepping up the dose, but it did little to ease his misery. The membranes that lined his intestines had eroded, and he suffered bloody diarrhoea. He died about twelve days after the explosion.

The injuries of the victims depended on how they had been contaminated. One firefighter had handled radioactive water. The worst burns were on his hands, which looked like he had blistered them in the sun. Other patients had inhaled burning fragments of plastic or radioactive gases. But exposure to radiation can be quirky. A Soviet doctor told a Moscow news conference that someone looking at an explosion in a nuclear plant could lose his left eye but not his right. A man's exposed hand might have to be amputated, but doctors would find no trace of radiation burns on the rest of his body.

The Soviet and American doctors were surprised by the pattern of injuries. Despite the fact that many of the patients were thought to have suffered less radiation exposure than cancer patients receive during standard radiation treatment, the damage to their soft body tissues was the worst Champlin had ever seen.

The most serious danger the victims faced was from infection. That was because radiation had destroyed the white blood cells that fight bacteria. And that was where Gale and his colleagues came in, with their expertise in bone marrow transplants. Marrow, a clear liquid that fills hollow spaces in bones, manufactures blood cells. About 3,000 bone marrow transplants are performed annually on leukaemia and anaemia patients. The transplants are among the most hazardous and intricate of organ grafts.

Gale, his colleagues and Soviet doctors performed bone marrow transplants on thirteen patients. The process involved extracting, a teaspoonful at a time, about a pint of bone marrow from a donor's pelvic bone, using a syringe. Close relatives make the best donors. The ideal bone marrow donor is an identical twin – a perfect genetic match. The Soviet authorities flew more than one hundred relatives of the Chernobyl victims to Moscow from as far away as Tashkent and Vladivostok for tissue-typing. The donated bone marrow was mixed with a soyabean extract called *lectin*, and injected intravenously into the Chernobyl victims. Six patients who had been so heavily irradiated that they did not possess sufficient white blood cells for accurate tissue typing received infusions of liver cells from miscarried or aborted foetuses. This experimental process depended on the capacity and foetal liver tissue to form blood cells just as bone marrow does and was used as a last resort.

The dangers of bone marrow transplants are manifold. The recipient can reject the new tissue. In addition, the transplant might reject the patient. What this means is that the donated bone marrow can kill the patient. In order to avoid this possibility, immune-suppressant drugs must be given. But this means that in the weeks following the transplant operations, the recipients are virtually without functioning immune systems, leaving them vulnerable to infection. Only after two to four weeks will the transplanted marrow start functioning.

Gale's assistance to the Soviet Union was given wide media coverage in the West, and he was received and thanked publicly by Gorbachev. *Pravda* printed a poem about him: 'God is in . . . Dr Gale, born the year of Hiroshima.' Gale became an international hero, recognised alike on the Moscow subway and in Beverly Hills restaurants. But, though they thanked him for his efforts, the Soviet physicians were disappointed by the result of the transplants. Only one of the thirteen patients who received bone marrow transplants lived.

Gale said it was the Soviet doctors who made the decisions about which patients would get bone marrow transplants, and he spoke of the serious condition of the patients on whom he had to operate. Reisner, while praising the Soviet doctors' attempts to save the victims, criticised them for showing 'poor thinking and poor planning' in failing to carry out immediate tissue-typing tests on the patients. Moreover, Reisner and the American doctors worked under handicaps. The Soviet Union was not geared up for bone marrow transplants. Gale had to take to Moscow high-tech medical equipment and medicines. Although Hospital No. 6 was a top Moscow hospital, Champlin said there was a critical shortage of technology, and the Soviet doctors had to work with equipment that was years out of date. There were frequent mechanical breakdowns. The hospital was in a poor state of repair and was not air-conditioned. Items the Westerners thought of as basic equipment were lacking: the hospital did not possess an automated blood-cell counter. With the counter, standard equipment in many Western haemotologists' offices, blood counts can be determined in twenty seconds. But the Soviet lab technicians still counted blood cells under a microscope, a process that took thirty minutes. However, the Moscow hospital and the Soviet doctors clearly had experience in handling cases of radiation exposure. The American doctors said the experience of the Soviet doctors was more extensive than theirs, and a report by the IAEA's International Nuclear Safety Advisory Group commented:

> It appears essential to stress the fact that the degree of success in the medical handling of patients with acute radiation syndrome depended critically on the availability of a centre, in Moscow, highly specialised in the diagnosis and treatment of the sickness. The experience gathered there in preceding years in treatment of individual accidental cases and patients irradiated for medical reasons proved to be of immense value as it resulted in the availability of the specialised personnel, facilities and techniques.[9]

The reference to 'individual accidental cases' raised the question of whether the hospital had previously dealt with victims of accidents at nuclear power stations. Did the hospital gain some of its expertise treating victims of the Kyshtym nuclear accident in the late 1950s? They are intriguing questions, but ones that are not likely to be answered.

Dr Angelina Guskova, a radiation biologist in her sixties and the senior physician at Hospital No. 6, said in Vienna in August, 1986, that the transplants 'actually did more harm' than good. She said she was 'depressed' at the outcome of the transplant operations because she had expected them to work. She told a medical writer for *The Boston Globe* newspaper that Gale 'is young and it is easier for those of us who are older to recognise that we are being led in the wrong direction.'[10]

Guskova said that the medical teams at Hospital No. 6 also became discouraged because of the severity of the injuries they were treating. She said that 'physicians were weeping: they said it's impossible to go on. I had to cheer them up, to tell them not to show inner emotions to others because you are doctors.' The patients were not told about deaths among their numbers. In order to explain the disappearance of those who died, the living were told that they

had been transferred to other hospitals. But it is unlikely
they believed this.

The immediate death toll from the Chernobyl disaster
was thirty-one. The victims were buried in two rows in a
special area of the sprawling Mitinskoye cemetery thirteen
miles west of Moscow, in graves marked with white marble
headstones. Gold inscriptions gave the names and dates of
birth and death of the victims. Two of the headstones bore
women's names. There was no plaque or marker to say that
these were victims of the world's worst nuclear accident.
But a space was left in the front row of the tombstones,
perhaps for a monument.

*   *   *

The firemen, plant engineers and others buried at the
Mitinskoye cemetery were among the first victims of the
Chernobyl disaster. Radiation biologists said many other
people will die prematurely in the years ahead, not only in
the Soviet Union but across Europe. They will die of cancer
caused by nuclear fallout. The pattern of that fall-out was
dictated by where the wind blew and the rain fell in late
April and the beginning of May. When the Soviet Union
gave its report on the Chernobyl disaster to the International Atomic Energy Agency, the complexity of the
pattern of radioactive release and dispersion became clear.

The radioactive plumes from the wrecked reactor rose
high into the atmosphere and were driven by the winds over
a wide area of the Soviet Union, Eastern and Western
Europe. Radioactive material from Chernobyl continued
to spew into the atmosphere for nine days. The largest
releases of radioactivity were on the first day, and other
major releases took place on May 4th and 5th after the
nuclear reactor had begun to heat up again.

What was in the plumes? Analyses of air samples collected by Soviet planes the day after the accident showed
a number of radioactive isotopes, including zirconium^{95},
tellurium^{132}, ruthenium^{103}, neptunium^{239}, and caesium^{137}.

Traces of plutonium were found on the ground nearby the reactor.

People living and working in areas under the plumes received doses via direct external radiation from the plume, by inhaling radioactive particles and gases, and by external exposure to the fallout. People also received doses of radiation through swallowing contaminated foods or liquids. The fact that the Chernobyl accident happened at a weekend, when the power station was running with a reduced staff, and at night, when people were in bed, limited the external exposure dose of people in the immediate neighbourhood. The height attained by the plumes also cut down on the doses they received.

The nature of the radiation risk depended on: the dose of radiation to which people were exposed, and its type, the type of radiation emitted, the nature of the radioactive substances to which they were exposed, and the organs and tissues of their bodies where the radioactive elements concentrated.

The most immediate concern was iodine[131]. Iodine[131] is volatile and forms a vapour, which may be inhaled, or which may collect on grass and plants. If cows eat iodine-contaminated grass, the iodine will be found in their milk. The most usual ways of absorbing iodine[131] are through drinking contaminated milk or breathing iodine vapours. Once in the body, the iodine concentrates in the thyroid gland. The thyroid, located in the neck, absorbs iodine to support its natural function – the production of the hormone which regulates body growth and the body's metabolism. Children were particularly vulnerable to contamination from iodine[131] because their thyroids were small and still growing. Contamination of the thyroid raises the long-term risk of contracting thyroid cancer. But the iodine[131] began decaying rapidly. Iodine[131] has a half-life of eight days. After six months it reduces to less than one millionth of its initial amount.

More worrying in the long-term was caesium[137]. This isotope has a half-life of about thirty years. A report prepared by the World Health Organisation immediately after the disaster spoke of 'unexpectedly high' deposits of caesium[137].[11]

Caesium[137] from fallout settled on the surface of plants and leafy vegetables and would enter the food chain when people or livestock ate the contaminated plants. But the caesium would be dangerous for years because it can also enter plants through their roots (although the transfer of caesium[137] from soil to root is slow). Caesium[137] can remain in the food chain for many years.

The behaviour of caesium[137] in the environment is fairly well understood from studies of fallout from atmospheric nuclear weapons tests in the 1950s and 1960s. The United Nations Scientific Committee on the Effects of Atomic Radiation (UNSCEAR) has published a number of reports which assessed the radiation doses from the fallout. Caesium was the most common contaminant. Caesium[137] was found in milk, meat and cereals. Shellfish also absorb caesium[137]. (Some fishermen who eat catches taken from the Irish Sea near the Windscale reprocessing plant in northern England absorb about 0.2 rem a year from fish contaminated by caesium[137].) Wild berries, mushrooms, honey and lichen are also particularly susceptible to contamination.

Another isotope in the radioactive plumes that drifted from Chernobyl was strontium[90]. Soviet scientists said in their report presented to the IAEA in August, 1986: 'With time, it is possible that this nuclide will be of basic significance together with caesium[137].' Strontium[90] emits beta radiation and is therefore more difficult to detect than caesium[137] which emits gamma radiation. Strontium[90] is a close analogue of calcium and may be deposited in bones. It can remain in soil for generations. But monitoring of radioactive fallout in Britain failed to detect any strontium[90]. Barrie Lambert, a radiation biologist at St Bartholomew's Hospital Medical College, London, doubted that strontium[90] fallout would be a problem.

* * *

The releases from Chernobyl did not occur as a single event. Instead, both the rate of release and the direction the radiation was carried varied over the nine days that Chernobyl continued to spew radiation. A provisional report on the Chernobyl accident by the European regional office of the World Health Organisation on May 6th grouped the radioactive release into five periods:[12]

1. Area: **Scandinavia, Finland, Baltic**.
Emission: April 26; arrived April 27–30.
2. Area: **Eastern Central Europe, Southern Germany, Italy, Yugoslavia**.
Emission: April 27; arrived April 28–May 2.
3. Area: **Ukraine and eastwards**.
Emission: April 28–29; arrived April 28–May 2.
4. Area: **Balkans, Romania, Bulgaria**.
Emission: April 29–30; arrived May 1–4.
5. Area: **Black Sea, Turkey**.
Emission: May 1–4; arrived May 2 and later.

Television and newspaper maps in the early days of the disaster showed a 'cloud' moving uniformly across places like Sweden and Poland. But the reality was that areas only a few miles apart received vastly different amounts of fallout. Just a road or a few fields were enough to separate areas of high radioactive fallout from areas of low radioactivity. The deposition pattern depended on rainfall.

This phenomenon was noted by World Health Organisation scientists who said that radioactive levels in local 'hot spots' were often ten, or even fifty, times higher than average radioactivity levels in surrounding areas. Two months after the accident, WHO officials stressed that the average levels of radioactivity in almost every European country were very low indeed but that levels in localised hot spots of heavy fallout concentration gave some cause for concern. The rain and winds created these hot spots in parts of north-central Scandinavia, north-east Poland, southern Germany, north Wales, Scotland and north-western England. But the worst hot spots were in the Soviet Union.

The first radioactive plumes were driven directly to Finland, where they arrived within twenty-four hours. Radioactivity was detected at the Kajaani monitoring station in Finland on the evening of April 27th after a rain shower. The early material blew over Scandinavia for three days.

Heavy rain brought down fallout over some areas of Sweden between April 27th and 29th. The pattern of the rainfall was patchy, with high levels around Uppsala and north of Stockholm. One of the worst affected places was the city of Gävle, on the Baltic coast about a hundred miles north of Stockholm. The rain in Gävle began at 6.30 on the evening of April 28th. It poured all night then slackened about seven in the morning, having drenched the docks, the two paper mills, the schools and fields with almost an inch of water. The rain soaked the town with iodine[131], caesium[137] and fourteen other radioactive isotopes. When the people of Gävle awoke, radiation levels were eighty times normal. Gävle was the worst contaminated area in Sweden and one of the worst in Western Europe. Yet,the city of Uppsala, an hour's drive away, received much less radiation, and Stockholm received hardly any.

Sweden's radiation institute calculated that about as much radiation fell on Sweden after Chernobyl as during the entire period of American and Soviet atmospheric nuclear testing. The institute calculated that the average Swede would absorb an additional millisievert of radiation over the next three decades, and that some Swedes, such as those in Gävle, would get up to five additional millisieverts. From natural sources, each person in Sweden normally receives one millisievert a year. Extrapolating from these figures, some Swedish experts calculated that, over the next thirty years, up to one hundred Swedes would die of Chernobyl-linked cancer, and fifty additional babies would be born with birth defects. Environmental groups said these figures were too low and that the number of cancer deaths could reach 3,000 over the next thirty years.

One tragic consequence of the radioactive fallout over both Sweden and Norway was that tens of thousands of reindeer were contaminated by caesium. Swedes and Norwegians were warned against eating reindeer meat. The susceptibility of reindeer to caesium contamination was due to their feeding almost exclusively on lichen, which soaks up rain like a sponge and retains radioactivity in its foliage. The reindeer would have to be destroyed. In Sweden, there were plans to feed the contaminated reindeer to fox and mink in fur farms.

There was other damage, too. Pike, perch and trout in thousands of lakes in Scandinavia showed high levels of caesium contamination, and people were warned not to eat too much fish. Lingonberries, Arctic raspberries and tiny yellow cloudberries, a delicacy which grows in swamps, had to be kept from the market. In Norway, high caesium readings over a wide area of the country suggested that cattle, elk and even bears had been affected. Thousands of tons of vegetables were found to be contaminated, and traces of strontium^{90} were found in milk.

North-east Poland was squarely in the path of radioactivity from Chernobyl. The worst contaminated place was Mikolajki, a lakeside town of 3,500 people located about 400 miles north west of Chernobyl. When residents of the town recalled April 28th, all they could remember was that the weather was beautiful, with brilliant sunshine and crisp spring winds. There were rumours of high radiation counts at the local monitoring station, but local people thought the equipment had failed. Later, Polish officials disclosed that radiation levels at Mikolajki on April 28 were 500 times greater than the usual background level. Local people complained of gastric disorders, an affliction they attributed to radiation sickness although it was probably psychological in origin.

Zbigniew Jaworowski, head of the Department of Radiation Hygiene at the Polish Central Laboratory for Radiological Protection in Warsaw, said later that a quarter of Poland was 'highly contaminated' by fallout.[13] He said high doses of radiation were found among people who drank contaminated milk. Jaworowski said that in the heavily contaminated region of the country, thyroid radiation doses were measured in 1,200 people, both adults and children. He said the average dose was estimated to be from one to ten millisieverts. In a limited number of cases, thyroid doses measured in adults were about one hundred millisieverts and in children about 800 millisieverts. By one estimate, a dose of 800 millisieverts could be expected to double the incidence of thyroid cancer. Since the incidence of thyroid cancer is normally about one per million people, that would mean that for every million people who received those doses, about two thyroid cancers would develop.

Southern Germany was another area which received high fallout from Chernobyl. Heavy rainfall drenched the beer gardens, pavement cafés and parks of Munich on the afternoon of April 30th. A British scientist, Simon Goodman, who was working at a laboratory near Munich trooped outside with his colleagues at 4 p.m. that afternoon and monitored the wet grass. It was so radioactive the monitor went off scale. Goodman commented: 'That night it rained hard. Hard like cats and dogs; hard as sung about by Bob Dylan.' Soil samples taken in parts of Bavaria in June 1986, turned up caesium concentrations hundreds of times higher than normal. Some Bavarian farmers kept their livestock indoors away from radioactive pastures. West German studies consistently found heightened levels of caesium[137] in game meat, mushrooms, fresh water fish, berry fruits and dairy products. In most cases, officials said the levels were not high enough to cause concern.

Heavy rain also fell on April 30th and May 1st across south-eastern France, Switzerland, Austria and Czechoslovakia. Some months later Swiss authorities banned fishing in Lake Lugano because the fish had been poisoned. Swiss farmers were urged to reduce the amount of green fodder fed to livestock. Switzerland retained a 'recommendation' against drinking sheep or goats' milk from the south of the country for months after Chernobyl, especially for children under two and pregnant and nursing women. In Northern Italy, authorities ordered hundreds of thousands of caesium-contaminated rabbits slaughtered. In parts of Austria, authorities were still counselling caution about eating leaf vegetables months after the accident. In the Netherlands, caesium deposits on some vegetables were found to be fifty times the usual range, although the health ministry said there was no cause for concern.

Radioactive plumes from Chernobyl reached Britain on May 2nd. They crossed the south-east coast of England and blew towards the West Country before turning north and travelling over Wales, Cumbria and Scotland. Heavy rain fell on May 2nd, 3rd and 4th. This rain washed the fallout from Chernobyl onto thousands of sheep farms. On June 20th, almost two months after the reactor erupted, the British Government announced that the rains had so polluted the grasslands where spring lambs were feeding that many lambs had radioactivity levels higher than those permitted for consumption. The government put a ban on the movement and slaughter of sheep and lambs in parts of North Wales, the Lake District and two areas of Scotland.

In Scotland alone, almost 1.5 million sheep and lambs on nearly 2,400 farms were affected. In Wales, 5,100 farms with more than two million sheep and lambs were covered by the ban. Tens of thousands of lambs were kept from the market in England. Many areas were freed from the restrictions within a few weeks or months, but, in other areas, bans remained in place. Dr David Horrill, a research scientist for the government-supported Institute of Terrestrial Ecology, said that monitoring showed that the problem of polluted sheep should soon be over. As late as December, though, the ban had not been entirely lifted.

Horrill's institute started monitoring what happened to the fallout once it was washed off the grass. The goal was to find out if caesium would pose any long-term dangers to grazing livestock.

The British Department of Health said in a report on Chernobyl that the nuclear disaster was likely to trigger some increase in cancer deaths over the next half-century. It said a more precise prediction would have to await concrete data on how much Chernobyl fallout Britain absorbed. Michael O'Riordan, of Britain's National Radiological Protection Board, said between forty and forty-five people in Britain might die from cancer as a result of Chernobyl fallout. The extra death estimates had to be compared with the 1,300 deaths a year caused by natural background radiation. Environmental groups said the government figures were too low.

The last plumes of radioactivity from Chernobyl blew east and south, across the Ukraine, the Balkans, Romania, Bulgaria, Turkey and the Black Sea region. Fallout from the winds that blew over eastern Turkey contaminated the tea and hazelnut crops. Radiation levels in hazelnuts in the worst-hit provinces of Giresun, Ordu and Trabzon along the eastern Black Sea coast were unacceptable by standards of the European Economic Community. Some Greek peaches and apricots showed high caesium[137] readings, and the Greek Government urged vigorous washing of vegetables and fruit. It maintained a warning against drinking fresh goat milk.

One of the saddest health effects of Chernobyl was the unknown numbers of pregnant women in Eastern and Western Europe who had abortions because of fears that their children would be born deformed.

* * *

The long-term health and environmental problems for Western Europe were minor compared with those of the Soviet Union. Many thousands of people in the Ukraine and Byelorussia were directly exposed to radiation from gamma and beta rays and from nuclear fallout deposited on towns, villages, farmlands, livestock, forests and water supplies.

An IAEA report estimated that doses to most people in the nineteen-mile exclusion zone around the wrecked reactor were less than 250 millisieverts.[14] But some people received doses of 300 to 400 millisieverts or more. Thyroid doses from iodine[131] were estimated to be mostly below 300 millisieverts. But some children may have received thyroid doses as high as 2,500 millisieverts. It was not known how many pregnant women were among the evacuees. There were rumours in Moscow of large numbers of abortions in the Ukraine and Byelorussia after the accident. For days afterwards, until measures were introduced to restrict consumption of foodstuffs, people drank milk contaminated by iodine[131]. They ate vegetables that had been dusted by caesium[137]. Village wells were poisoned. Even flowers were a hazard.

*   *   *

How many people will die in the Soviet Union and the rest of Europe from premature cancer as a result of radiation exposure from Chernobyl? Estimates ranged from a few thousand premature deaths all the way up to half a million. A grim debate about numbers went on for many months after the accident.

The Soviet report on the medical consequences of Chernobyl said:

Taking into account the fact that spontaneous deaths from cancer over a seventy-year period for the 114,000 evacuated people [Soviet estimates of the number of evacuees varied widely] may be about 14,000 cases, the natural death rate from cancer among the exposed population will be increased by less than two per cent as a result of the accidental release from the Chernobyl plant.[15]

The estimate suggested that about 280 additional cancers would occur among this group of evacuees over the next seventy years. The report also suggested that there would be 4,750 deaths from premature cancer among people not

in the immediate danger zone around the reactor. There
would also be 1,500 cases of thyroid cancer. Normally,
about one or two of every ten thyroid cancers is fatal in
Western countries. Soviet scientists estimated that cancer
mortality rates in the Ukraine and Byelorussia might increase by 0.4 per cent as a result of people eating caesium-
contaminated food.

Some Western experts disputed the Soviet estimates and
said they were too low. In particular, they said that the
Soviets had failed to take sufficient account of the long-
term contamination of the food chain from caesium[137].
Other Western scientists complained about what they said
was the confused and incomplete data presented by the
Soviet Union. They took issue with the Soviet report on the
medical consequences of the accident. That report stated:

> Thus there is no danger to [the] health of the population
> living outside the thirty-kilometre [nineteen-mile] zone
> around the Chernobyl plant resulting from the levels of
> external gamma radiation of the products released dur-
> ing the accident. A more complex situation arises when
> estimating doses of internal exposure resulting from
> the intake of radionuclides through consumption of
> contaminated locally produced food products.[16]

Two nuclear experts, Dr Morris Rosen, the American
director of the IAEA's division of nuclear safety, and Dr
Dan Beninson, an Argentine who heads the standard-
setting International Commission on Radiological Protection, arrived at a figure of 24,000 premature deaths in the
European Soviet Union as a result of Chernobyl. They
reached this figure according to a formula by which it was
assumed that one additional cancer death would be caused
for every 10,000 man-rems of exposure. (A man-rem is a
way of calculating the exposure of populations to radiation.) By their calculation, 24,060 people would die from
the 240.6 million man-rems of radiation in three zones of
the Soviet Union – the 19-mile exclusion area, a second

zone comprising a large area of Byelorussia and the Ukraine and a third zone comprising the whole European area of the Soviet Union. The methodology assumes that a given dosage of radiation will cause a certain number of cancer deaths. Once the dosage is known, the rest is a matter of calculation. But Beninson and Rosen caused a stir in Vienna when they retracted their estimates just a day after they had given them. They said they had misunderstood the Soviet data, and the excess cancer death figures would probably be much lower. Beninson put the eventual figure at 5,100. Rosen said it might be in the range of 10,000.

The highest death estimate came from Dr John Gofman, Professor Emeritus at the University of California, Berkeley, and a long-time researcher into the effects of low-level radiation. Gofman was one of the discoverers of uranium[233] and isolated the world's first workable plutonium for the Manhattan Project. He estimated that 424,300 people in the Soviet Union and 526,700 people in Europe and elsewhere would develop cancer over a seventy-year period. He said another 19,500 people would develop caesium-related leukaemia and an unknown number would develop thyroid and other cancers from other radioactive materials in the fallout. He said half the cancer cases would be fatal.

Gofman had long argued that since the dose-effect relationship between radiation and cancer is linear, any dose of radiation, no matter how infinitesimal, heightens the long-term risk of contracting cancer.[17] In other words, there was no harmless amount of radiation exposure. He argued that even a dental X-ray carries a heightened risk of cancer. On this hypothesis, a near-zero exposure to radiation produces a near-zero effect, not a zero one. Critics of Gofman said that he was over-estimating the risks of low-level radiation. Dr Arthur Upton, a former director of the US National Cancer Institute, said: 'Dr Gofman has a history of exaggerating risk estimates for radiation.' Other radiation biologists did not go along with Gofman but they said that permissible dose rates for workers in the nuclear industry were set too high and should be lowered.

The effect of low-level radiation exposure is one of the most politically charged issues in science. However, the Chernobyl victims may help clear up the mystery. The Soviet Union announced plans to monitor the health of people around the reactor site for the next seventy years in what would be one of the largest and most extensive medical studies in history.

8

HEROES AGAINST OUR WILL

Life will win the day. For the black-and-white stork standing by its nest on the roof of one of the abandoned houses is waiting and waiting for people. There will be people, flowers and weddings in Chernobyl.

Sovetskaya Rossiya, May 14th, 1986[1]

One of the first problems facing the Soviet Union after the nuclear accident was how to evacuate tens of thousands of people in areas of the Ukraine and Byelorussia around the Chernobyl power station. There was criticism in the West because Soviet officials delayed thirty-six hours before going ahead with the evacuation of Pripyat, the town adjoining the power plant. But was this criticism fair?

Soviet sources told Western nuclear experts that the main routes out of Pripyat were more heavily contaminated than the town itself so it made sense to wait until they had located safe evacuation routes by radiological monitoring. Certainly, the way in which the Soviet Union coped with the huge evacuation programme over the next weeks showed some of the strengths of the Soviet system.[2]

As the scale of the emergency became apparent, about 135,000 people were evacuated from the towns and rural areas around Chernobyl. Eighty-six thousand farm animals were shipped out in hundreds of trucks. The evacuation was carried out in several stages, and reports suggest that people were still being moved out of areas within the nineteen-mile exclusion zone as long as ten days after the accident.

About 1,000 families living in a workers' settlement only one mile from the plant were apparently evacuated by local transport about twelve hours after the accident. But the 49,000 people of Pripyat and three other villages near the stricken reactor were not evacuated until thirty-six hours after the reactor blew up although the order for the evacuation was apparently given by Ukrainian Deputy Premier Konstantin Masik on the evening of April 26th. Parents in Pripyat sent their children to school as usual on the morning of April 26th, hours after the roof of the reactor blew off. But some residents were swift to realise the scale of the emergency. Misha Telyatnikov, aged ten, and his brother, Oleg, twelve, the sons of the Chernobyl fire chief, later remembered that their mother roused them at 3.30 a.m. 'Wake up,' she told them, 'We are going to Kiev.' Other residents of Pripyat also fled.

The great majority of the townspeople stayed put. Later, at a holiday camp near Yalta on the Black Sea, some of the Pripyat children remembered on the morning of the accident seeing the fire-blackened reactor surrounded by a misty cloud. They also remembered trucks watering down the Pripyat streets. At school, their teachers instructed them on the steps to be taken against radioactivity: 'Stay inside when you get home, tape up the windows, close the balcony doors, wash your shoes and change your clothes.' Olya Demidova, aged fourteen, said that the children were given iodine treatment at school, and lessons about civil defence were taught again. Another child, fourteen-year-old Oleg Zorin remembered: 'At school we were told: listen to the radio. There may be an announcement.' Volunteers went from house to house handing out potassium iodide tablets.

Soon after midnight on April 26th a fleet of 1,216 Kiev city buses and 300 trucks started moving north from the Ukrainian capital, some of the drivers having just finished their regular shifts. The convoy was more than twelve miles long. The drivers entered the danger zone around the Chernobyl plant at 2 p.m. on April 27th. Members of

Komsomol, the Young Communist League, had already visited every apartment block, listing everyone living there and telling people what to do. They told the evacuees to take little luggage and not to use private cars to prevent traffic jams. Some people did not want to leave. A delegation of Pripyat residents went to see the Ukrainian Deputy Minister of the Interior, Major General Gennadiy Berdov, to protest against the evacuation of the town. There were angry scenes.

The buses drew up outside the apartment blocks and within two hours and thirty-five minutes the evacuation was complete. Leaving the area, the buses were stopped at periodic roadblocks, and police with geiger counters came aboard to check radiation readings on clothing. The Kiev city buses were washed down before they were returned to passenger service.

After the evacuation, rumours circulated in Moscow that many of the bus drivers swigged from vodka bottles as they entered the danger zone, supposedly as a prophylactic measure against radiation. The story was that, with sufficient vodka inside, the human body was between one and one a half times more resistant to radiation. Another remedy said to be effective against radiation was to add strong red wine, a drop at a time, to a glass of vodka and then drink the glass in one swig.

After the evacuation, police searched all Pripyat's apartments to see that everyone had gone. The town's 10,000 children, including 3,000 infants, were taken directly to summer camps in the Ukraine and other Soviet republics. Soviet reports hinted at emotional scenes of distraught parents and crying children. Some parents had to be persuaded to part with their children. Three weeks after the accident, some Pripyat children did not know their parents' whereabouts. Some people were still searching for their relatives weeks later. The Kiev region Communist Party chief, Grigory Revenko, said in an interview a few days after May Day: 'There was some lack of coordination, basically of an organisational character, in providing the evacuees with the basic necessities, especially in clothing and footwear.'[3]

Not until almost a week later was the six-mile exclusion zone widened to nineteen miles. For the first few days the 12,500 residents of the town of Chernobyl, ten miles south-east of the power plant, went to work as usual. But anxiety in Chernobyl and surrounding villages about radiation levels mounted as the days wore on. The decision to expand the exclusion zone came on May 2nd after a visit to the area by two senior members of the Politburo, Premier Nikolai Ryzhkov and party propaganda chief Yegor Ligachev. In ordering the exclusion zone to be widened they gave the impression of overriding those who had been previously in charge. The second stage of the evacuation brought to 92,000 the number of Ukrainians moved out from around the ruined reactor. Another 26,000 people were evacuated from Byelorussia. Thousands more would join them as more radiation danger spots were discovered. The scenes were reminiscent of the Second World War when people in European Russia fled east to escape the advancing Germans. But now the enemy was invisible.

Evacuating the farms turned out to be more complex than getting the townspeople out. Entire farms, with their equipment and animals, were trucked out. Each collective farm from the exclusion zone was billeted on a host farm. One of the organisers of the evacuation later told an *Izvestia* reporter:

A few old women took some persuading. They even hid in their cellars. You would find them there and they would say: 'My dear. Just look how the orchard is blossoming. Who will look after it? Who is going to feed all the chickens and ducks? They would never forgive me.'

The sudden arrival of tens of thousands of people put a huge burden on those who were asked to receive them.

Workers in country stores, cafeterias and service establishments worked two or three shifts to handle the sudden influx of people. Village shops gave credit for food and clothing. Supplies in the receiving areas were strained. Village schools which received older children introduced shift teaching systems. Medical services worked at full stretch. More than 1,200 doctors, 920 nurses, 3,000 medical assistants and 700 medical students provided health care for the evacuees and tested them with radiation counters. By one Soviet estimate, 18,000 people were briefly treated in hospital after the nuclear disaster. The evacuees were not suffering from radiation-related illnesses, but from the psychological stress caused by fear of radiation, the upheaval of the evacuation and concern over relatives. Some children were hysterical.

The evacuation from the exclusion zone was only the first stage of a vast scattering of people caused by the Chernobyl disaster. Thousands of people fled the city of Kiev. For a week after the accident, residents of the Ukrainian capital treated the Chernobyl accident lightly. But the calm turned into near-hysteria after Ukrainian Health Minister Anatoliy Romanenko appeared on television to announce that the wind had changed and it was blowing towards Kiev. He said there was no cause for alarm, that radiation levels had risen only slightly, but that it might be 'a good idea' if people closed their windows, took showers, washed their hair daily and scrubbed their apartments. He also said that children up to the age of ten were to be evacuated from the city, and they, and breastfeeding mothers, should stay inside.

The result was panic. Kiev's streets were deserted except for roads to the railway station and airport. Crowds queued at ticket halls in desperation to leave the city. Extra trains were put in service. Parents scrambled to put their children onto trains to Moscow and other places where they had relatives. People snapped up books about nuclear fallout and radiation. Then, the Kiev authorities announced that schools were to be closed ten days early for the summer holidays and that children would be evacuated to their traditional summer camps early. In mid-May, an estimated 250,000 children left Kiev. Pregnant women and mothers with infants also left.

Evacuations of communities in Byelorussia and the Ukraine were still going on two and a half months after the nuclear accident. Some areas that were evacuated were many miles outside the nineteen-mile exclusion zone. Alexander Petrov, deputy premier of Byelorussia, told *Pravda*:

Clean areas [of Byelorussia] were found within the thirty-kilometre [nineteen-mile] zone and, at the same time, individual "dirty spots" were found beyond its boundaries.

It was therefore difficult to assess the size and exact location of the contaminated areas outside the nineteen-mile exclusion zone because the wording in Soviet press reports was ambiguous, and geographic references were often unclear. One badly affected area in Byelorussia was the region around the city of Gomel (population 350,000) which lies about ninety miles north of the Chernobyl power station. Sixty thousand children were sent away from the Gomel region in June. Infants were sent away with their mothers or kindergarten teachers. Officials reported that there were radioactive hot spots in two other Soviet republics – Moldavia and the Russian Federation. They let it be known that many of the evacuees from the worst-contaminated zones might not be allowed to return to their homes any time soon.

Officials thought that Pripyat would be uninhabitable for years. A team of drivers collected hundreds of private cars from Pripyat and returned them, after decontamination, to their owners. Many Pripyat people returned to the town in June, 1986, for brief supervised visits to pick up belongings and family documents left behind in the rush of the April 27th evacuation. The town's apartments were sealed off, and burglar alarms were placed in the apartment blocks to deter looters. A graphic Soviet report spoke of dogs roaming wild in the empty streets and foxes devouring untended chickens.

*   *   *

Three months after the accident a reporter from the Soviet Baltic Republic of Estonia was given an unenviable assignment. Tonis Aavikson was dispatched to the Chernobyl region by special bus to report on the activities of a group of 200 to 300 Estonian workers who had been conscripted into a clean-up effort at a site near the Chernobyl plant. He travelled to the area with an Estonian rock band which had been ordered to go to play for the workers. The musicians spent the journey apprehensive about exposure to radiation.[4]

Aavikson found that the men had been set to work decontaminating the Chernobyl area, washing houses and trees in villages, stripping the topsoil, loading it onto trucks and replacing it with soil that had been trucked in from outside. The men had been ordered to remove a full ten centimetres of topsoil along with bushes. The men wore protective clothing and face masks. Radiation dosimeters hung around their necks. Living conditions were grim. They were accommodated in tents with wooden bunks. They rose at 6 a.m. and, after breakfast, were driven to the decontamination site, from which they returned only at 8 p.m. They had two rest days a month. The men were discontented and demoralised. Some said they had been taken from their jobs and sent to Chernobyl. They had been working at the site since soon after the accident. They worried about exposure to radiation. Aavikson described their mood as 'one of indignation, extreme bitterness and despair.' Conscripts from other parts of the Soviet Union were also working at the decontamination site.

Aavikson wrote about the men in a series of articles for

Noorte Haal, the Estonian-language daily of the *Komsomol* Youth League. The articles were unusually frank. The articles were apparently meant to be reassuring, but, reading between the lines, they gave a different impression. In one article, Aavikson said that a number of men had suffered health problems because of exposure to radiation and because they were spending cold nights in makeshift tents at the end of scorching days.

The conscripts feared that they might become sterile from the radiation. 'More than several men,' reported Aavikson, 'were worried that plans made with a girl or a recent bride just before departure could in this confused world easily go awry.' At another point, Aavikson criticised a superior who kidded one of the Estonians about the pointlessness of a conjugal visit by his wife. 'Making strained jokes about relations between the sexes,' wrote the journalist, 'was like shaking a hornet's nest.' Rumours circulated in Estonia that the men were drinking heavily. Aavikson dismissed the rumours of massive alcohol consumption at the site, but, revealingly, he said that there had been instances of moonshine liquor sold to the men by local peasants at one hundred roubles for a three-litre bottle.

If the men received high doses of radiation, it qualified them to be sent home. Aavikson implied that some men volunteered to work in the most contaminated areas around the Chernobyl plant in order to be sent back to Estonia immediately. He said: 'Only some individual volunteers will go, for example, to Pripyat once, where the radiation level is still high. In one shift they can receive a dose [that results in] their being sent home.' He mentioned one case where a man tried a ruse on his superiors. Aavikson reported that:

One man left his dosimeter for a couple of days in the dust near the zone close to the reactor. Then he collected it, hung it around his neck and in the evening showed his superiors that [his dose] was over twenty roentgens and asked them to think about sending him home.

But, the report continued, the man's designs were 'easily seen through.'

In June the Estonian conscripts were told that their two-month tours of duty had been extended to six months. This caused bitterness, particularly since reports suggested that they and their families had initially been told that they were going to Chernobyl for only thirty days. According to Aavikson, the men gathered angrily en masse to demand an explanation. This seems to have led to a scuffle:

> In the beginning, around 200–300 men went to demand clarification of the announcement. They heard what they had already known. There was one case in which someone was grabbed by the collar as well as some jabbing of knees into buttocks and throwing of sand. Otherwise, no force was used. So said the men themselves, even though at home there are also stories about larger fights.[5]

Aavikson's description of what happened was vague. It was not clear who jabbed whom. It was not clear how order was restored. But Aavikson left no doubt that the situation was tense:

> The air was filled with strong words that were fuelled by disappointment, indignation, despair and the general tangle of feelings. In their impetuosity, the men did not even remember where they were or how it might all end. There were nevertheless those who calmed the ones who were too hot-headed and the tale ended without a larger scandal. The men dispersed.

The confrontation led to a work stoppage which seems to have extended into July. Aavikson said that reports of the 'uprising or the strike' were extremely exaggerated in Estonia. But he said that the news of the work extension:

> ruined the men's willingness to work, creating a psychologically explosive situation. For a while some men

simply stood idle, having worked like oxen before. The normal work rhythm was restored bit by bit, and by the time we were there in mid-July everything in this respect was back in order.

Aavikson said that the men felt like 'squirrels in a running wheel . . .' He said: 'At Chernobyl, he [a man] has nowhere to go and can only choose to swallow his bitter fate.'

After the story was picked up in Western newspapers Aavikson was quoted by the *Novosti* news agency in September as saying that 'not one Estonian has died or fallen ill from radiation sickness.' But private reports from Estonia claimed that a junior lieutenant in the reserves died in August from radiation exposure at the site. He was named as Gunner Hagelberg (or Hakelberg), a graduate of the Tallinn Polytechnic, who was reportedly conscripted in the street to take part in the clean-up operation.[6]

The Soviet media said that everyone who laboured in the Chernobyl area was a volunteer. In Vienna, Valery Legasov, the head of the Soviet delegation to the IAEA deliberations, laughed off the *Noorte Haal* reports. He said: 'We have ten times as many volunteers as needed.' The Soviet news agency *Tass* denied that any strike took place and took offence at a *Voice of America* story about the Estonians.

Clearly, the Soviet authorities had no alternative after the Chernobyl disaster but to set men to work in hazardous conditions. These workers showed remarkable courage and resolution in the face of the danger from radiation. But Soviet media reports stressing the selflessness and exemplary behaviour of workers, particularly Communist Party and *Komsomol* members, generally ignored problems of morale. Workers were depicted as front-line fighters in a war against the hidden enemy of radiation. The media made frequent comparisons with the heroism of Red Army troops in the Second World War. Alexander Prokhanov, in the daily *Sovetskaya Rossiya*, wrote:

In that very place, in the accident zone, in the zone of maximum danger, I saw shining, voluntary record-speed work . . . so dear God, don't give us more Chernobyls.

The Estonian conscripts saw their contribution in a different light. They referred to themselves as 'heroes against our will.'

* * *

The experience of the Estonian conscripts – washing trees, hosing down houses, shovelling up soil – underlined the awesome environmental problems facing the Soviet Union. Soviet scientists estimated that about half the radioactive materials from the wrecked reactor fell within the nineteen-mile exclusion zone around the Chernobyl power station. Many farms and villages were uninhabitable. Crops, forests, lakes and rivers were poisoned. The Soviet Union learned the hard way how to cope with a nuclear accident.

The Chernobyl station itself was highly radioactive. Workers were able to enter the plant only for short periods. Four months after the accident, radiation levels were still so high that decontamination crews could work only three hour shifts. In some radiation-soaked areas of the plant, according to the *Sovetsky Patriot* newspaper, 'even the minutes are counted.' The newspaper said: 'Today at the station the motto is "Maximum safety and minimum risk." But to be frank it is impossible to work here without risk. . . .' Workers used remote-controlled bulldozers and cranes to move earth and shift concrete.

The initial explosions strewed the surrounding area with intensely radioactive debris – parts of the damaged reactor, bits of the building that were blown off and other structural elements. Nuclear scientists said the debris should be entombed in concrete containers and buried like the nuclear waste from a power plant.

Radioactivity levels were high for miles around the plant.

But readings showed sharp variations owing to the uneven deposition of fallout. The military and police set up road blocks and checkpoints and special passes were required to enter the contaminated areas. The road blocks displayed signs: 'Danger zone, entry forbidden.' Supplies were transshipped from 'clean' lorries onto 'dirty' ones at the road blocks. Some evacuated farmers tried to sneak back to tend their private gardens and attend to chores. (One Central Asian, who had been advised to seek radiation treatment for radiculitis – inflammation of the nerve endings – sought to expose himself for therapeutic purposes to elevated background levels of radiation around the Chernobyl plant.)

An immediate hazard for workers in the contaminated areas was radioactive dust. The authorities went to war against dust. Troops in protective suits hosed down buildings, gardens and trees with water, and used polymer sprays to trap radionuclides and prevent them being resuspended in the atmosphere. The polymer liquid trapped the dust and dried into a film which was collected and taken away for disposal. Helicopter pilots flew over the plant, spraying liquid synthetic rubber and water over dusty areas. Drivers bringing supplies to Chernobyl were warned not to walk on the verges of roads in case they kicked up radioactive dust. In some villages, entire areas were covered over with asphalt or paving stones.

Ukrainian health officials warned sun-seekers not to stir up dust or lie directly on the beaches of the Dnieper River, which flows through Kiev. The newspaper *Izvestia* advised in June: 'One more rule is added, a rather important one. It is not recommended to play football and volleyball on the beaches at the moment, because the dust is kicked up during the playing.' In Kiev, officials assured housewives that radiation levels posed no threat to health but advised them to wipe dust away with a damp cloth and to limit the time young children spent outdoors. More than three months after the accident, trucks still rumbled along the *Kreshchatik*, Kiev's tree-lined main avenue, spraying water to wash away radioactive dust. In the central department store, rubber-booted elderly women sprinkled water on the floor with straw brooms. People entering public buildings in Kiev stepped on water-soaked cloths to remove dust from their shoes.

The authorities cautioned people not to eat food grown on private plots or locally-produced vegetables. Produce was brought to central points and checked with geiger counters. Officials decided whether to bury contaminated food or release it for processing. They reimbursed farmers for lost produce with tinned food. Officials paid particular attention to checking milk. Milk contaminated by iodine[131] was thrown away or stored to allow the iodine to decay.

For months after the accident, officials ran geiger counters over food on sale in farmers' markets in the Ukraine and Byelorussia. Red and black currants, gooseberries and mushrooms were banned for sale. Some food was thrown away because there were not enough inspectors to check it. Four months after the accident, produce sold in Kiev markets was still being tested every day at special laboratories. As far away as Moscow, shoppers shunned food from the Ukraine and Byelorussia.

A major decontamination operation took place in the Byelorussian town of Bragin, about fifty miles north of Chernobyl. Soviet officials said radiation levels there warranted an evacuation. But with tens of thousands of people from neighbouring areas of Byelorussia already evacuated, the strain on emergency housing and services was immense. Officials decided to evacuate children and mothers from Bragin (population 7,000) while most adults remained in place. The chairman of the town council told a Soviet journalist:

> We could never have coped without the army. We had to wash down carefully all 1,220 houses, hundreds of barns and garages and tens of thousands of trees. We did not want to cut them down and leave Bragin bald for the future.

Some moss-covered older buildings that could not be easily decontaminated were torn down.

The town authorities made difficult decisions about where to bury radioactive topsoil that was bulldozed from the streets of the town and where to put shrubs and rubbish that had soaked up radiation. Workers laid new asphalt on all the streets, pavements, squares and the land near schools and kindergartens, and they cleaned and sealed 169 water wells. Two new artesian water wells were drilled and connected to the town's water supply. Unexpected problems emerged: it was found, for instance, that cow dung and other animal manure was particularly radioactive, and special provisions had to be made for its disposal.

A picture emerged of an enormous engineering and manpower effort. But this decontamination work was not very effective. *Pravda* reported in July 1986, that forty-one villages in the Bragin area were still too dangerous to be reoccupied even after two months of effort. Soviet officials said they hoped that people would eventually be allowed back into the Chernobyl area. Some experimental farming was started in the late summer of 1986 (the farmers were rotated every ten days), and plans were announced to let 260 families back into three decontaminated hamlets in the nineteen-mile exclusion zone.

But Western scientists said there would be long-term radiological consequences if people lived on, or farmed, contaminated land. One Western expert said: 'You don't want generation after generation sitting on contaminated land, continually exposed to it.' One problem is that long-lasting radioactive elements like caesium^{137} and strontium^{90} get into the food chain by moving through the roots of crops and hence into animals or humans who eat the crops. The clean-up teams tried to deal with this problem by stripping off topsoil, but it was clearly unrealistic to strip the topsoil off the surface of the entire nineteen-mile exclusion zone. Moreover, the disposal of radioactive topsoil was a problem.

The area around the Chernobyl plant was unsuitable for

the disposal of radioactive soil. The soil has a high sand content deposited by melting waters from retreating glaciers in the last Ice Age. Sand allows radionuclides to filter into the groundwater. Clay soil is better for waste disposal: clay soils bind radionuclides into their structure and prevent infiltration. Western experts said the ideal site to store the earth would be an arid location with little rainfall. They said desert areas would be the best location.

Agronomists came up with plans to attempt to return the farm land to production. One idea was to fertilise the contaminated land with lime and ashes and then turn over the topsoil by deep-ploughing it. Supporters of this measure said it would prevent radioactive elements rising to the surface again. Scientists suggested that farmers should consider growing rye rather than wheat since rye absorbs less radioactivity.

Was the Soviet Union too optimistic about resuming farming? Nigel Bell, of Imperial College, London, spent six years studying the likely routes by which radioactive contaminants enter the food chain. He thought it would be more than ten years before the radioactive material released from the Chernobyl reactor would cease to be a problem for farmers. 'Close to the reactor I think they will have enormous problems,' he said. A twenty-year study of nuclear fallout from the atmospheric nuclear tests of the 1950s and 1960s found that contamination of soil was a long-term problem. The study by Dutch ecologists suggested that two-thirds of all the fallout from the nuclear tests that was deposited at sampling sites in north-west Europe was still present in the top ten centimetres of soil.[8]

Another problem was contaminated forests. Trees tend to trap radioactivity. Environmentalists warned of the dangers of forest fires since these could spread radioactivity over a wide area. Soviet officials spoke of the need to improve fire protection in the Ukraine and Byelorussia. Even the leaves of the chestnut trees on the streets of Kiev were trucked away for disposal after they fell to ground in autumn.

From the earliest days of the Chernobyl accident, scientists worried about contamination of water supplies. One of the first tasks of troops sent to Chernobyl was to build a cofferdam along the banks of the Pripyat River near the power station to prevent contamination from the site from washing into the river. Engineers built a complex system of boreholes and barriers around the nuclear power station to stop underground streams reaching the most radioactive zone where the water could pick up radioactive material. From the first days of the accident, heavy AN-12 planes flew many missions, spraying clouds with silver iodide and other chemicals – the cloud seeding was to make sure no rain fell on the Chernobyl region. *Radio Moscow* said this measure practically prevented rain in the nineteen-mile exclusion zone for many weeks after the accident.

Publicly, officials issued calming assurances about water supplies, but it was clear they were worried. Engineers built an entirely new alternative water supply system for Kiev. The project included building a new pumping station to tap water from the Desna River and laying two four-mile-long conduits to bring the water to the Kiev city reservoir. The pipelines were laid in record time across roads, bridges, tunnels and, in some stretches, under water. The object was to instal the new water supply before autumn when floods could overwhelm the defences around the Chernobyl reactor. All factories in Kiev, from bakeries to milk bottling plants, were linked to emergency wells sunk deep into the city's bedrock.

The scale of efforts to cope with the aftermath of the Chernobyl disaster was awesome. Officials drew up plans to build fifty-two new villages in two regions near Kiev to house the evacuees. The building programme, involving more than 50,000 construction workers, included plans for 7,250 houses. Construction workers began building another 4,000 homes for evacuees in Byelorussia. Planners started work on a new township to house 10,000 displaced Chernobyl power station workers on the banks of the Kiev reservoir. Workers completed a twenty-two-mile road between this new town and the town of Chernobyl in just two months. Engineers built a new bridge near Chernobyl, and new port facilities were constructed on the banks of the Dnieper River. Building materials and equipment were shipped in from all over the Soviet Union on special trains, fleets of trucks and river barges. A nineteen-ton bulldozer was flown to Kiev from Chelyabinsk in the Urals aboard a wide-body IL-76 cargo plane. A 200-ton automated crane was fitted with lead shielding in Leningrad and sent to Chernobyl. Power station workers were provided with temporary floating homes aboard eight ships anchored at river berths.

A Politburo report in July, 1986, estimated the direct cost of the Chernobyl accident at about two billion roubles. But the indirect cost of sealing the wrecked reactor, safeguarding water supplies, supporting the evacuees, building entire villages of new homes, schools, stores and medical centres and decontaminating more than 1,000 square miles of farmland and villages, was incalculable. No Soviet report ever stated how many workers were brought to Chernobyl from all over the nation to help in this massive programme. But some Western journalists estimated that the total must run into hundreds of thousands.

Scientists said that the region around the reactor would have to be subject to strict radiological surveillance for many years. They said that the soil, animals, plants, insects, mammals, fish and other forms of life in this area would contain significant amounts of caesium[137]. Environmental groups in the West said that external and internal radiation might threaten the survival of some species, or cause mutations in animals and plants. A September, 1986, report for the IAEA gave this grim warning: '. . . it is evident that there will be visible effects on terrestrial and aquatic plant and animal life close to the Chernobyl reactor site.'[9]

* * *

It is not surprising with so much damage and so much disruption that there was a search for those who were to blame. There was plenty of guilt to go around.

At the top of the list were the Chernobyl plant's director and the chief engineer. The director was fired and the engineer was expelled from the party for his negligence and for conducting unauthorised tests. The party secretary at the Chernobyl plant branch was ousted from his post, and the first secretary for Pripyat town was said to have been severely punished. The party had been embarrassed by the fact that as late as June, 177 of the more than 2,600 party members from Pripyat could still not be located. One man was reported to have fled all the way to Odessa, from where he sent a telegram asking for his back pay.

In Moscow, the disaster led to a shake-up in the management of the nuclear industry. At least four officials were dismissed from their posts, including the chairman of the State Committee for Safety in the Nuclear Industry, the first deputy minister of electric power (who was responsible for the nuclear power industry) and the deputy director of a nuclear reactor research design institute. Also removed from office was the first deputy minister of medium machine building. The Medium Machine Building Ministry is in charge of nuclear weapons and the production of nuclear reactor fuel.

Other consequences of the accident were the creation of a separate ministry for nuclear power and the introduction of a nuclear inspectorate, charged with making sure safety standards are maintained.

*   *   *

The children of Kiev returned to the city at the end of August, 1986, from camps and resorts across the Soviet Union from the Carpathian Mountains to Armenia in Transcaucasia. It was just like the start of any other school year except that geiger counters were now part of the standard equipment of the city's 295 schools.

In at least one maths class, the basic lesson was: 'The smallest atom bomb equals three Chernobyls.'

9

NO ONE THOUGHT IT COULD HAPPEN

It hit us unprepared in Europe. Even measurement systems were not in place. There was considerable confusion.

Jo Avsall, European Regional Director,
World Health Organisation[1]

The scene in the crisis response centre set up outside Stockholm after the Chernobyl disaster was chaotic. Jack Valentin, a Swedish radiation safety official, said later: 'It was bloody hell in this room.' Banks of telephones, military radios and telexes hummed day and night. Charts and maps lined the walls of the room, and yellow, orange and white markers charted the direction of the radioactive plumes and the pattern of nuclear fallout. Officials from the War Department, Civil Defence, Nuclear Safety, Meteorology and Radiation Protection departments worked round the clock. Few people had time to sleep. The Swedish officials did their best to share with the Swedish public the little they knew about the nuclear accident that had taken place more than 1,000 miles away at the Chernobyl nuclear power station in the Ukraine.

There were similar scenes in crisis centres in other European capitals in the days after Chernobyl. The nuclear accident caught European governments by surprise, and their response was slow and confused. The problem everywhere was inadequate planning. The single most important lesson of Chernobyl for Europeans was that Europe was not prepared for nuclear accidents.[2]

Some governments told their citizens quite a lot about the radioactive plumes that drifted across Europe at the end of April and beginning of May. But others said almost nothing or even kept silent and only disclosed radiation readings long after the radioactive clouds had dispersed.

European governments responded to the emergency in an uncoordinated and chaotic way. There were inconsistencies in the way they measured radioactive fallout and in the way they reported their findings. Public health precautions varied. The levels of admissible radiation in foodstuffs differed sharply from country to country and even from region to region. Even within governments there was confusion, with different agencies issuing conflicting statements. Advice given to the public at national levels contradicted advice given at local levels. One senior World Health Organisation official in Copenhagen admitted later that communication between experts and the public was 'terrible.'[3]

Politicians used Chernobyl as an opportunity to make tortuous comparisons between 'safe' nuclear power in the West and 'unsafe' nuclear power in the East. Environmental groups said the accident justified their calls for the abolition of nuclear power. Nuclear industry officials played it down. Journalists contributed to the anxiety and confusion with sensational reporting. One screaming headline in the *New York Post* read 'Late Word from inside Russia: Mass Grave for 15,000 N-Victims.'

Governments put the need to prevent panic above the need to inform their citizens. Political, economic and trading considerations were allowed to outweigh health considerations. The information policy adopted by some governments was dictated by a determination to prevent a backlash against the nuclear industry. A report for the Rainbow Group of the European Parliament said:

In the period after the Chernobyl disaster questions of public health and limitation of risk were often dealt with irresponsibly. 'Risk' turned out to be an elastic concept, with people's safety being sacrificed in many cases to the effort to minimise the domestic political damage from Chernobyl.

The report said the continuing clash between health protection and politics became evident at two levels – at the international level in the East–West confrontation, and at the national level through the confrontation between governments and their critics. The report concluded that:

It turned out not to be a very big gap that separated Soviet secrecy and shortage of information from similar shortcomings on the part of Western governments.[4]

*   *   *

A Brussels-based consumer watchdog group made a study of how the twelve member states of the European Community responded to Chernobyl. Its report said, 'All countries took steps to monitor radiation in the environment and foodstuffs and to check imports from Eastern Europe, but this is about where the common ground ends.' The report singled out France and Belgium for particular criticism – 'it is significant that those countries with the highest dependency on nuclear power tended to do the least' – but it also blamed West Germany and Italy for allowing economic considerations to influence their actions.[5] The Rainbow Group report said: 'The way the French authorities kept quiet for the first fourteen days [after the accident] exactly matched the secrecy on the Soviet side.'[6]

South-eastern France was contaminated by fallout from Chernobyl. Some areas showed readings of 300 to 400 times the normal level of background radiation. Yet Pierre Pellerin, head of the Centralisation Service for Protection against Ionising Radiation, maintained that there was no hazard to health. Only after two weeks did Pellerin change his tune. He admitted that radiation readings had not been disclosed in order to prevent panic. Some French people responded angrily. Didier Anger, the leader of the Greens, an environmentalist party, said: 'We learn that radiation levels have fallen back to normal. But they never told us that they were ever too high.' A headline in the left-of-centre daily, *Liberation*, read: 'France, the European red light for information.'

France depends on nuclear power for sixty-five per cent of its energy. (The figure for Belgium is sixty per cent, Sweden forty-three per cent, Switzerland forty per cent, West Germany thirty-one per cent, Spain twenty-two per cent, the United Kingdom twenty-one per cent, and the United States fifteen per cent.) France, remarked Lord Marshall of the British Central Electricity Generating Board, 'has four natural advantages in support of nuclear power: no oil, no gas, no coal (and) no choice.'

In West Germany, there was total confusion after Chernobyl. Politicians and officials at national, regional and local levels bombarded an anxious public with conflicting advice. Some state governments recommended much stricter radiation precautions than those recommended by the Federal Government. In Baden-Württemberg, for instance, officials closed public playgrounds, banned the sale of leafy vegetables and told parents not to let their children play on the grass. Environmental groups published their own radiation readings in a bid to show that official figures had been fixed too low.

Mainline politicians claimed that the Greens party was using the crisis to create unfounded hysteria. The Greens responded by accusing politicians of minimising the nuclear danger. The head of the West German radiation protection agency, Dr Erich Oberhausen, said that some precautions recommended by environmental groups were an absurd over-reaction. But environmentalists claimed that measurements had shown astronomical levels of caesium^{137} and iodine^{131} in animals. What were West Germans to make of all this? One opinion poll found that sixty-one per cent of the West German population changed their purchasing and living habits on account of Chernobyl.

In Britain, Environment Secretary Kenneth Baker told the House of Commons that if there were no further radioactive discharges from the Chernobyl reactor, the effects of the disaster should be over for Britain within a week. That proved one of the most optimistic statements of the year. On June 20th, almost two months after the accident, the government announced that spring rains had so polluted grasslands in the Lake District, parts of North Wales, and areas of Scotland, that over one million lambs and sheep might have radioactivity levels higher than those permitted for consumption. Strict controls on transport, sales and slaughter of the animals were ordered. Some people in Britain took their own precautions. The mayor of Winsford in Cheshire ordered the withdrawal of fresh milk from thirteen primary schools, reasoning – 'it's better to be safe than sorry.'

Italy thoroughly confused its citizens. Officials first announced that fallout had reached the country on April 30th, but then changed the date to April 27th. The government emphasised there was no danger, but Italians cleared supermarkets of tinned and frozen foods that had been packaged before Chernobyl. Officials published only average figures for radiation levels; they did not publish maximum readings. About a week after the disaster, Italy imposed tough internal bans on the sale of leafy vegetables. The bans prompted spirited protests. When police seized vegetables from shops near Rome's Piazza del Popolo, two young tradeswomen stripped themselves naked, donned artichokes for cover, and challenged police to arrest them. The police officers obliged. On the island of Ischia in the Bay of Naples, Maria di Meglio filed a civil lawsuit against Soviet President Andrei Gromyko asking millions of lire in damages for the loss of her vegetable crop. She also demanded that Gromyko should appear before the Ischia magistrates to face up to his responsibilities. Italy's minister of civil protection, Giuseppe Zamberletti, lamented: 'Is it really credible that Sardinian vegetables were contaminated, but those from Corsica were not?' He was referring to the two neighbouring Mediterranean islands, the first Italian, the second French, which had taken different precautions.[7]

Chernobyl forced Swedish authorities to re-examine their emergency response plans for a nuclear accident. The plans covered only the immediate area around nuclear plants. Thus, only four out of twenty-four Swedish counties had adequate contingency plans to cope with fallout. One Swedish radiation safety official said the spread of radioactivity more than 1,000 miles from an accident site was 'not theoretically unknown . . . It was in the books. But, until Chernobyl, no one assimilated the message; no one thought it could happen.'[8]

Concern for health appeared to be secondary in the EEC wranglings over banning imports of fresh food from Eastern Europe. It was clear from the clumsy way in which the EEC imposed the import bans that political and economic considerations had been put above health considerations. The bans covered food imports from areas up to 630 miles (1,000 kilometres) from Chernobyl. But East Germany was excluded from the ban at the insistence of West Germany. Yugoslavia was included in the ban at the request of Italy. Austrian produce was not covered by the ban although part of Austria fell into the zone.

Teddy Taylor, a British member of parliament, underlined the absurdities of the ban in the House of Commons on May 8th when he asked a junior Foreign Office minister, Timothy Eggar:

How can you justify the exclusion of East Germany from the ban, when parts of East Germany are much nearer to the disaster than parts of Czechoslovakia and Yugoslavia?[9]

How indeed? Eggar responded that the greater part of East Germany was outside the area of the ban, and it would be up to West Germany to check the origin of foodstuffs coming across its frontiers. Understandably, the East European countries saw the EEC moves to ban their food as a restrictive trade measure.

The EEC also failed to agree on a single standard for admissible levels of radioactivity in food traded within the Community. Instead, member countries agreed to respect each other's norms. Again, it seemed that trading considerations were taking priority. Community officials said privately that wrangling over the food radiation levels had embarrassed Western Europe and indicated that it might be impotent when faced with a major crisis. 'If we cannot agree on this, what else can we agree on?' said one. Lynda Chalker, a minister at the British Foreign Office, said: 'It looks bad if we cannot come to a decision.' An EEC official added: 'It's a pity that we cannot act quicker.'

East European governments did not behave any better. The Rainbow Group report said all East European governments adopted a policy of issuing reassuring statements which minimised the danger of fallout from Chernobyl. The report said:

> Measurements of radioactivity were kept secret or released in dribs and drabs. Yet at the same time full measurements were made available to the IAEA and other foreign and international organisations. It looks as though one of the reasons for this was concern about export interests.[10]

Initially, the state-controlled media in the East European countries followed Moscow's policy of a near-total news blackout on Chernobyl. Their first reports on the accident merely echoed the Soviet communiqués. Later, there were differences in what East European governments told their citizens, and how much they told them. Poland, closest to the accident, kept its people best informed.

Czechoslovakia's rigidly orthodox and strongly pro-nuclear power government said almost nothing.

Poland suffered the most serious contamination from radioactivity of any country outside the Soviet Union, and it took the toughest anti-radiation measures. Health workers dosed about ten million children with iodine preparations. The Poles prepared emergency plans to evacuate people from radioactive areas in thousands of railway coaches, buses and trucks. Two hundred extra radiation monitoring stations were set up. In western Poland, schools and hospitals were designated as possible quarantine centres for radiation victims.

Polish scientists appeared repeatedly on television in an effort to reassure an apprehensive public that radiation levels were well below the danger level. A special government commission issued daily bulletins which acknowledged contamination of air, soil, surface water, milk and fresh vegetables. But a warning about possible contamination of fresh vegetables was issued only after a delay of several days.[11] The Polish information policy had severe limitations. Figures supplied by the Polish Government to the IAEA showed that radioactive contamination from Chernobyl reached higher levels than the Polish people were told.[12] The authorities released figures for average levels of radiation in Poland, whereas they told the IAEA of maximum levels of radiation.

Many Polish women had abortions despite official reassurances. Unofficial sources in Poland privately estimated that several thousand women sought abortions in May and June because of fear of radiation-induced birth defects. A Warsaw paediatrician was quoted as saying:

> There is no question that many women are having abortions because of Chernobyl. It is very sad, but they are afraid, and what can you tell them?[13]

One rumour which swept Warsaw in the middle of May was that rain had washed radioactivity into the Vistula River and that contaminated water was heading for the city in a lethal tide. The city's water pressure dropped as people filled bathtubs. The Czechoslovak Government did not acknowledge any increase in radioactivity levels until May 5th.

*　　*　　*

The first lesson of Chernobyl, agreed nuclear experts, was that emergency response plans had to be coordinated across Europe. Ian Waddington, chief environmental officer at the World Health Organization in Copenhagen, said: 'Emergency plans have to cover the whole of Europe – we're all in this together.'

The World Health Organisation and the IAEA discussed a number of improvements. Officials said among the priorities were uniform standards for measuring radiation and determining its health effects and an international treaty calling for immediate and full reporting on accidents at nuclear power stations. Soviet officials said they would sign such a treaty. The WHO agreed to set up a European information service for nuclear accidents and said it would seek ways of improving international coordination to limit the effects of nuclear fallout. After Chernobyl, officials across Europe recognised the need for better communication with a confused and frightened public. Lord Marshall of the British Central Electricity Generating Board pointed out that even the basic language to talk about radiation was lacking:

> We describe radiation in terms of curies, becquerels, rads, rems, sieverts, grays, and by the milli, micro and pico versions of those units. I am myself a rads and rems man. I cannot understand the other units, and if I cannot understand them, how can I expect the public to do so?

Chernobyl prompted demonstrations and protests across Europe against nuclear power. Many Europeans regarded the accident in the Soviet Union as proof that nuclear power was fundamentally unsafe and that the nuclear industry in all countries could not be trusted. The protesters called for the closure of nuclear power stations and the abandonment of plans to build new ones. No country was untouched by this mood of environmental protest.

The backlash against nuclear power was felt within days of the accident. Thousands of people demonstrated in twenty West German cities. Some 100,000 demonstrators marched through the streets of Rome calling for nuclear power to be phased out. Chernobyl had an almost immediate impact on European politics. In the May 4th Austrian presidential elections, an outsider, a candidate for a fringe ecology group, finished a surprising third. In Sweden, popular pressure grew for accelerating plans to phase out all nuclear power by the year 2010. In Switzerland, lobbying revived against the building of any more nuclear reactors. European politicians hastily backed away from nuclear power commitments. In Austria, the government ordered the dismantling of the country's only nuclear power plant at Zwentendorf, west of Vienna. The plant had been standing idle since a 1978 referendum which narrowly decided against putting it into operation. Before Chernobyl, politicians had talked of holding another referendum. After Chernobyl, it was decided to dismantle the reactor without further delay.

Some anti-nuclear campaigners staged headline-catching stunts. In Sweden, protesters took several tons of hay which had been contaminated by fallout and dumped it at the prime minister's office. In Austria, members of Greenpeace climbed Vienna's towering Ferris wheel and displayed a banner: 'Stop nuclear power now.' Some forty West German environmentalists trekked up the country's highest mountain, the Zugspitze, to protest against plans to build a nuclear reprocessing plant in Bavaria.

There was a curious inwardness about the European response to Chernobyl. Anti-nuclear protesters soon turned their attention away from the Ukraine and instead focused on the nuclear power programmes of their own countries. Europeans showed their concern about the disaster by demonstrating not outside Soviet embassies but outside European nuclear power plants. In West Germany, 30,000 people marched on the Brokdorf nuclear power plant, some forty miles north of Hamburg. There were similar demonstrations in other European countries.

The lesson of Chernobyl was that radioactivity knows no frontiers yet many demonstrators tackled the nuclear power issue in purely national terms. Pierre Lellouche, of the French Institute of International Relations, was right when he said:

> Everywhere in Europe people turned their worry – and anger at being left in the dark – not against the author of the accident, but against their own governments and their own nuclear programmes.[14]

For many Europeans, Chernobyl was a symbol rather than a reality.

*   *   *

Supporters of the nuclear power industry fought a difficult battle. In Britain, television commercials attempted to put over the message that nuclear power plants were reliable, safe and clean. One commercial showed a nuclear power plant in the midst of idyllic countryside. The commercial seemed to be asking people to picnic at the plant. A supporter of nuclear power in West Germany was so irritated by constant criticism of nuclear power that he said in exasperation: 'In our country, a jumbo jet could crash-land on a nuclear plant and nothing would happen to the reactor.' Nuclear industry spokesmen tried to get over the message that burning fossil fuels instead of using nuclear energy would increase the incidence of lung cancer and other diseases. But, in the post-Chernobyl climate of fear, people were not in a mood to hear that message. Opinion polls after Chernobyl showed a marked swing in Western Europe against nuclear power.

Although Chernobyl was a major domestic crisis for Gorbachev, it brought him some unexpected international dividends. The accident deepened the opposition of European left-wing parties to nuclear power and nuclear weapons, and strengthened the convictions of nuclear disarmers. Chernobyl probably benefitted Britain's Labour Party leader Neil Kinnock and his plan to fight the next general election on a pledge to get rid of Britain's nuclear weapons and remove all American nuclear bases.

Chernobyl also strengthened the left-of-centre Social Democrats in West Germany. A Christian Democratic politician neatly pointed out the irony of this: 'It would be a paradox of German parliamentary history, if because of an accident in a technically inadequate Soviet nuclear reactor, the left, of all people, were to triumph.'

* * *

Across Eastern Europe there were signs of an unprecedented debate about nuclear power. People took part in spontaneous demonstrations and signed petitions. Scientists voiced doubts in public about nuclear energy. The most vigorous protests were in Poland. On May Day, riot police in Warsaw broke up a crowd of demonstrators chanting 'Ukraine, Ukraine.' In Wroclaw, about 200 demonstrators marched through the streets, some of them carrying placards asking: 'Is an atomic death from the East any different?' At a demonstration in Cracow, a young Pole held up a banner on which was scrawled: 'Chernobyl is everywhere – except in the East.'

In Czechoslovakia, an unofficial organisation called *Anti-atom* was formed in response to Chernobyl. (Among the Warsaw Pact countries, Czechoslovakia is second to the Soviet Union in its dependence on nuclear energy). Some 300 East Germans signed a petition to the government and parliament calling for the scrapping of plans to build East Germany's third nuclear power plant. A statement by the Cracow branch of the banned Solidarity movement summed up the feelings of many East Europeans about 'The Cloud' that drifted over their countries at the end of April and the beginning of May: 'Once again, political goals were valued over people's health as was evident when children and young people were obliged to attend official May Day parades.'

It was unusual for an environmental issue to prompt such a show of feeling in Eastern Europe. Moreover, ordinary people got involved in the demonstrations. In Wroclaw, mothers with pushchairs demonstrated. But the demonstrations were not so much about nuclear power as about censorship. East Europeans were angered by the silence of their governments after the accident and wanted assurances that if there were another Chernobyl they would be told about it. The demonstrations were unwelcome to East European governments because they called into question both the governments' concern for their citizens' health and the relationship between the East European countries and the Soviet Union. Moreover, all the East European countries are committed to expanding the role of atomic energy in electrification.

* * *

One question that interested Soviet analysts was what effect Chernobyl would have on the attitude of the Soviet people towards the environment. Could Chernobyl lead to the 'greening' of the Soviet Union? Could it be a spur for the emergence of an environmental movement that would eventually exert political pressure on the party and government? Could party leaders be forced to take account of environmental pressures from below?

In fact, there was already a vocal environmental movement in the Soviet Union, and support for environmental causes had been growing. One leading Soviet analyst describes the movement as made up mainly of scientists but backed by strong popular sentiment.[15] He said the movement is weakly organised but has gained some surprising coverage in the Soviet media and has scored some environmental victories, notably against the pollution of Lake Baikal in central Siberia, hydropower schemes in the southern Soviet Union and the dumping of untreated wastes. This movement has roots in Russian nationalism. Above all, it is inspired by the need to conserve the countryside and to protect 'Mother Russia.' (One of the recent trends in Russian literature is the 'village movement,' a genre that depicts rural society as one of the great sources of Russian strength and virtue.)

The environmental movement has arisen partly in response to the careless treatment of nature over many years by Soviet planners, builders and engineers. Since the early days of the revolutionary state, Soviet planners regarded nature as something to be tamed and transformed in the fight to build Communism. A speech by Zazubrin at the first congress of Siberian writers in 1926 expressed the common view that 'old nature' must be torn down and refashioned:

Let the green fragile breast of Siberia be dressed in the cement armour of cities, armed with the stone muzzles of factory chimneys, and girded with iron belts of railroads. Let the *taiga* be burned and felled, let the *steppes* be trampled. Let this be, and so it will be inevitably. Only in cement and iron can the fraternal union of all peoples, the iron brotherhood of mankind be forged.[16]

The statement reflects the development-at-all-cost imperative which guided Stalin in his efforts to modernise the Soviet Union at a breakneck speed and without regard for cost. Stalin's planners, engineers and builders paid scant regard to the environment. Mining, tree-felling, railway and dam building were carried on without regard for any other criterion except meeting the demands of the Plan. Natural resources were squandered in huge quantities.

Coal, electricity, water, timber and oil were used with great inefficiency. The sheer physical size and low population density of the Soviet Union encouraged this attitude to nature. One Western scholar has written: 'There persists in the minds of officials and citizens alike the impression that the expanses of Mother Russia are infinite and her riches inexhaustible.'[17]

The showpiece of Stalin's efforts was the refashioning of the Volga River, the longest Soviet river west of the Urals. In the 1930s his planners began work on thirteen large dams on the Volga. Canals were dug and river channels enlarged. By 1937, Moscow was linked to the Volga and the Caspian Sea, as well as to the White and Baltic seas. The scheme was a triumph. Only later did Soviet scientists realise that the scheme and other land improvement projects had caused immense environmental damage.

Khrushchev inherited Stalin's careless attitude to nature. His disastrous Virgin Lands experiment was one of the greatest single acts of degradation of nature in history. Khrushchev's aim was to turn tens of millions of acres of *steppe* in Kazakhstan and western Siberia into the major bread-producing regions of the Soviet Union. Initially, the experiment was successful. But then the topsoil of millions of acres of land blew away in huge dust storms, reaching as far as European Russia.

A book published in the West in 1980 suggested that the extent of environmental damage in the Soviet Union was worse than scholars realised. The book, *Destruction of Nature in the Soviet Union*, was written by a producer of Soviet science films who used the pseudonym Boris Komarov.[18]

Komarov said Soviet planning agencies had adopted policies which had caused widespread damage to nature, and they had covered up the disastrous effects of their policies. He claimed that mining, logging, dumping and erosion had laid waste about ten per cent of the habitable land of the Soviet Union. Largely because of air pollution, the incidence of lung cancer had doubled between the 1960s and late 1970s. He said that the small Sea of Azov, adjoining the Black Sea, had become 'a latrine' with levels of oil pollution reaching one hundred times the officially permitted concentrations. Komarov said chemical effluents were destroying the unique eco-system of Lake Baikal; that wildlife reserves were being plundered; that the killing of wild animals and birds, encouraged by the shortage of fresh meat, was virtually uncontrolled. He wrote of inland lakes and seas drying up, of serious coastal erosion, of rivers poisoned by industrial effluent, of dwindling fish stocks and lost cropland.

The Russian-language manuscript of the book circulated in *samizdat* – secretly-published copies – in the Soviet Union. It is thought to have influenced many people to take an interest in the environment. It was almost certainly read by the people who make up the environmental movement in the Soviet Union.

The environmentalists' biggest victory so far was the fight to save Lake Baikal. It is the world's deepest lake – in places it is more than one mile deep – and it is several hundred miles long. According to some estimates, it holds one-fifth of the world's fresh water. People in Irkutsk, the nearest major city, say that Baikal water is so pure that it is almost distilled and can be used in car batteries. The lake contains unique forms of life and is a complete and self-perpetuating eco-system. More than 700 of its 1,200 living organisms are peculiar to Lake Baikal. They include 30,000 *nerpa*, the world's only fresh-water seals.

A decision by Soviet planners in the 1950s to bring industry to 'Sacred Baikal', in the form of cellulose and paper plants, touched off a storm of protest from a loose coalition of conservationists, scientists and writers. Eventually, the planners went ahead and built the plants. But the plants caused serious pollution in the lake. Logging added to the pollution problem. The threat to the lake caused many strands of opinion in the Soviet Union to unite. So great was the outcry that planners were forced to fit expensive waste filtration plants at the lake. They also ordered logging to cease. Today, Soviet officials are proud of the preservation of Lake Baikal and take foreigners to visit it.

Scholars say the Baikal affair was significant for two reasons. First, the defenders of the lake were able to get sustained media coverage and access to top policy-makers for fifteen years. Second, the battle for the lake established the precedent that it was sometimes possible in the Soviet Union to challenge a decision on environmental grounds.[19]

Early in 1986, the environmental lobby scored another victory when the Soviet leadership dropped plans to divert some of the country's rivers. The plan involved changing the northward flow of the great Siberian rivers to irrigate arid regions in Kazakhstan and Central Asia in the south. The project, which had two separate phases, would have ranked as one of the boldest manipulations of nature ever attempted. But Soviet and Western scientists warned that the project was a huge gamble with nature. They said it could bring the possible melting of the Arctic ice-cap, changes to the climate in the northern hemisphere and shifts in rainfall patterns. The abandonment of the plans was believed to be at the behest of Gorbachev who had shown a dislike of grandiose schemes.

Western analysts who have paid close attention to the stories of Lake Baikal and the river diversion schemes are now intrigued to see how the Soviet environmental lobby will respond to the massive radioactive contamination caused by Chernobyl. They are also interested to see if the Soviet leadership will pay more attention to voices advising caution on environmental matters and further expand the space allowed for open environmental debate. And there are signs of a growing willingness in government and the party to pay attention to the environment.

Even so, the old Stalinist attitudes die hard. Komarov relates the story of a debate within the Soviet Academy of Sciences in the 1960s about pollution of Lake Baikal. He quotes a first-hand account from a member of an investigating commission concerned about chemical pollution to the lake:

one old academician began to scream at us: 'But why are we going on so about this Lake Baikal? Pollute it if we have to. Now we have nuclear energy, and if later we have to, we can easily make a big pit and fill it with water and that's it. We'll make Baikal again.'[20]

10

ATOMIC POLITICS

The agency shall seek to accelerate and enlarge the contribution of atomic energy to peace, health and prosperity throughout the world.

Statute of the International Atomic Energy Agency[1]

When the Soviet Union acknowledged on April 28th that something had gone wrong at Chernobyl, it chose to announce the accident in the form of a telex message to an organisation many people had never heard of – the International Atomic Energy Agency.

That choice was entirely proper, since the IAEA is the closest thing the world has today to an international supervisory agency for nuclear energy. The IAEA is one of the many specialised bodies that has grown up over the years under the nominal sponsorship of the United Nations. Supporters of the agency like to call it the best of the UN agencies. Detractors usually refer to it as the most secretive. Both are probably correct.

The IAEA was established in 1957 at the end of the Cold War. Appropriately enough, its headquarters are in Vienna, the old capital of the Austro-Hungarian Empire, a city that today sits on the cusp between East and West.

Within the famous Ring – that wide imperial boulevard which encloses the old city – Vienna is dominated by Stephansdom, the cathedral, standing soot-stained and forbidding in the centre of a frivolous pedestrian plaza, where expensive shops sell all the glittering merchandise of the capitalist West. But there are other monuments, too, like the circular memorial the Soviet Union built to its soldiers who liberated the city at the end of the Second World War and who remained as occupiers until 1955 when the Austrian State Treaty gave the country back its independence. The Austrians, who are officially neutral, keep the monument in good repair, though they have planted trees around it to make it less visible from the street. Out at Sweichat Airport, the tarmac is dotted with traffic from East and West – a Lufthansa Boeing from Munich stands next to an Aeroflot Tupolev just in from Moscow. Off in another corner of the ramp, an ageing Romanian turbo-prop loads passengers for Bucharest while a sleek Swissair jet disgorges its cargo of prosperous businessmen looking for deals to make. When Soviet Jews win visas for Israel, their first touchdown is Sweichat. And more than one defector heading the other way has passed through the departure lounges, too, or through the Czechoslovak border post at Bratislava, only thirty miles or so from the city centre. If a visitor were to give in to romanticism on a rainy evening while walking in the narrow and twisting streets that snake off from the Dom, he might hear faint echoes of 'The Third Man' theme and imagine Harry Lime slipping into a shrouded doorway somewhere up ahead. Even today, Vienna is, beneath its veneer of tourist *gemütlich-keit*, a city where the line between East and West is blurred.

Once a year, the IAEA makes itself a part of this Vienna. The agency's annual conference is held at the Hofburg Palace on the Ring. There, ambassadors and government ministers from the 111 independent states plus the Ukraine and Byelorussia who are members of the IAEA gather for a few pleasant days of conversation and cups of Viennese *melange* coffee. For most of the year, the IAEA's Vienna is more pedestrian, a fifteen-minute subway ride away from the Dom, across the Danube at the Vienna International Centre, just across the street from a Chinese restaurant, a used car lot and a lake where sunbathers gather when the weather is good. The International Centre is one of those buildings only an architect could love, designed so that in the entire complex of structures there are no right angles, no straight lines. From the entrance, the visitor is confronted with three curving structures, two of them semicircles and the third a round, relatively low building. The semi-circular arms wrap around a huge grey and black courtyard with a fountain in the centre. The IAEA lives in the semi-circle to the left, an out-of-scale tower that rises to twenty-eight storeys. The concrete and glass façade is broken only by a slash of orange.

Inside, the corridors are colour-coded and marked with arrows. The windows do not open and the lifts don't necessarily serve every floor. To pass from one tower to another it is necessary to walk for hundreds of feet, sometimes even to go from floor to floor until a cross-over can be found. The walls are grey, the carpet muted and the lighting subdued. Metal partitions divide the workspaces. Perhaps the most confusing part of the complex is the central round building. The locus of power for the IAEA is there – the boardroom on the fourth floor. The conference building, one wag said, is a perfect metaphor for the United Nations because it is round, no matter where one starts from, if one keeps walking long enough in the same direction, one returns to the starting place. The metaphor – intentional or not – is a reminder that the IAEA is, in its essential nature, a political rather than technical body.

The agency came into being in response to the need for a way to make nuclear energy more acceptable to a world public that was becoming more and more alarmed by the growth of nuclear arsenals and by the continued testing of nuclear weapons in the open air. Though its statute envisioned an organisation that would grow to be a major supplier and controller of nuclear energy, the agency has never achieved those goals. Since the establishment of the Nuclear Non-Proliferation Treaty in 1968, the agency has carved out a particular niche – the administration of the safeguards programme that is designed to ensure that the world's non-nuclear weapons states stay that way. IAEA inspectors monitor the nuclear fuel cycle from manufacture to reprocessing to make sure that plutonium is not diverted from the process to enable a country to get the raw material to build a bomb. The safeguards programme is generally conceded to be a good one, though there are problems, not the least of which is the refusal of some states believed to be on the verge of producing nuclear weapons to allow IAEA inspectors to enter nuclear facilities.

There have been allegations that some states may have got around the inspectors. Other states, like Israel, are widely believed to have accumulated the plutonium to build bombs simply by stealing it. And Pakistan, considered to be one of several states just on the threshold of achieving nuclear weapons capability, is known to have run a well-organised and successful campaign to acquire the technology to build its own processing facilities to separate plutonium from spent nuclear fuel.

Countries like Argentina have refused to sign the non-proliferation treaty on the grounds that to do so would be to enshrine in law the feature of the treaty that requires only non-nuclear weapons states to open their nuclear power industry to outside inspection. The Argentines say they have no reason to build a bomb and no plans to do so; but to sign the treaty, they say, would be an affront to sovereignty.

Despite the problems, the non-proliferation treaty and the safeguards programme together have made it possible for the nuclear powers to sell their technology internationally without guilty consciences. A requirement that a nuclear plant be placed under the safeguards programme is a standard clause in sales agreements. Without safeguards, it is hard to imagine that an international nuclear industry could have developed. Without safeguards, the weapons states – which were also the main developers of nuclear power reactors – would have felt more constrained to limit access of other countries to a technology which can so easily be turned from ploughshares to swords. The IAEA's role in spreading nuclear power is crucial: as its statute says, its goal is to 'accelerate and enlarge' the role of atomic energy.

As such, it is not meant to be a neutral inspectorate or regulatory body but a nuclear energy promoter and a forum for nuclear power vendors to display the plants they have to sell.

Other than the occasional story claiming that there has been a failure of the safeguards inspections, the press pays little attention to what the agency does: a few journalists who work for trade publications follow the day-to-day operations of the agency. For general readers, the normal routine of the IAEA would make dull copy indeed. Usually, the agency is a focus of interest only because of its attempts to get South Africa or some other country to put nuclear facilities under non-proliferation safeguards. And the agency also takes up, at the instigation of Arab states, a debate on the 'Israeli nuclear threat.'

It had been business as usual at the International Centre during the first four months of 1986. But with the arrival of the Soviet telex, the IAEA was thrust into the most delicate political situation of its history – a full-scale nuclear disaster on the territory of one of its superpower members.

The challenge was fundamental – ever since the Three Mile Island accident in 1979, nuclear power had been increasingly unpopular. Now, with Chernobyl spewing radiation across Europe and almost no information emerging from the Soviet Union, the agency found itself on the front line of a public relations battle of unprecedented proportions.

The first step was simply to get some basic facts. In order to do so, a trip to the Soviet Union was hastily arranged for the top leadership of the agency, the Swedish director general, Hans Blix, his Soviet deputy, Leonard Konstantinov, and Morris Rosen, the American director of nuclear safety. The three men flew into Moscow, met Soviet nuclear energy officials and made a quick fly-over of the broken reactor. Back in Moscow, they negotiated a communiqué with their hosts that suggested that everything was under control. They managed to get the Soviet Union to agree to send to the IAEA radiation monitoring data from a string of observation posts. And they won Soviet agreement to report on the cause of the accident to the IAEA when it became known. It was a major step in breaking the silence.

In Vienna, the agency's board of governors was called into emergency session to consider what to do about the Chernobyl disaster. Before they could assemble, General Secretary Gorbachev finally spoke on Chernobyl in his May 14th address to the Soviet people. In that address, he called for the establishment of 'an international regime of nuclear safety.' That speech, which set out what the Soviet Union was willing to do in response to Chernobyl, largely determined the agency's programme of action in the coming months. In the speech, Gorbachev called for new international agreements on the swift reporting of nuclear accidents with international implications. This was an ambivalent response to Chernobyl. On the one hand, Soviet officials had maintained that they told the world about Chernobyl as rapidly as possible. But on the other hand, the call for a convention seemed to acknowledge that there was need for a better standard of behaviour. By the time the board of governors assembled for its emergency meeting, the outline of the international political response to Chernobyl was already emerging. It was a three-part strategy.

The first goal was to keep the Soviet Union talking about the accident. There was real fear in the early days after the accident that the Soviet Union would simply refuse to tell what had happened or would give so little detail that it would be impossible to determine what had caused the reactor to blow up. And nuclear experts were haunted by the fear that the Chernobyl accident – the world's worst nuclear power disaster – might have been caused by some hitherto unknown physical phenomenon. Finding out why the reactor had blown up was essential.

The second goal of the Western nuclear community was to place as much distance as possible between the Soviet nuclear programme and others, in order to be able to argue that what was wrong at Chernobyl was specific to the Soviet Union rather than a generic problem with nuclear power. The trouble was that this goal potentially interfered with the first one, since open criticism of the Soviet Union might well cause officials there to shut off the flow of information.

The third goal was to damp down the public fear that had spread with the nuclear plumes. The nuclear industry already had an image problem – years of wrangles over the siting of power plants and the dumping of nuclear wastes had done nothing to improve the image. The accident at Three Mile Island had stopped orders for new nuclear plants dead in the United States, potentially the biggest market in the world for reactors. Now, there were press reports that thousands of people would die of Chernobyl-caused cancers. Somehow, those frightening reports had to be counteracted if nuclear power was to have any future at all in countries where public opinion counted.

* * *

In the five months after Chernobyl, the IAEA held a continuing series of meetings where its delicate strategy was shaped and refined. Most of those meetings were closed to both press and public.[2] The agency was being true to its tradition of secrecy. The board of governors always meets in closed session with guards at the doors. Decisions are reached in the board after private negotiation. No votes are taken. Decisions are based on consensus, privately arrived at. Most documents are restricted. Even the list of names of the board of governors and ambassadors accredited to the agency is a confidential document.

The IAEA is dominated by nuclear power interests – hardly surprising for an agency whose charter enjoins it to promote nuclear energy. In 1986, twenty of the agency's thirty-five governors were employed by energy-related departments of their home governments. 'You won't find many "Friends of the Earth" types here,' said one of the more detached delegates. At a press briefing at the start of a special conference on nuclear safety in September 1986, Director General Blix was asked by a journalist if in fact the agency was not a mouthpiece for the nuclear lobby. Not so, he said, it was a mouthpiece for the member states. But later, he was heard muttering in an open microphone about the 'anti-nuclear lobby.' Just how sensitive the agency could be was revealed when security guards at the September safety conference attempted to confiscate from working journalists press releases they had been given by the environmental group Greenpeace. The agency's board of governors had earlier refused a request from Greenpeace for observer status at the safety conference. That status had been granted, however, to at least seven nuclear industry organisations, including the big American pro-nuclear group, the Atomic Industrial Forum. People inside the nuclear industry see the anti-nuclear groups as irresponsible; they say the anti-nuclear forces exaggerate the dangers of nuclear power. But by excluding these voices, the agency appears to operate as a closed shop.

Despite these limitations, with no western reporters getting in to see for themselves what was happening in the Ukraine, the attention of the international media turned to Vienna. The corridors around the board room on the fourth floor were filled with reporters and the occasional camera crew, all looking for some snippet of information. Since the question of what caused the accident was highly technical, while most of the reporters who had been sent to Vienna for the meetings were essentially political writers, they tended to focus on the political questions: why hadn't the Soviet Union reported the accident sooner and what was the agency going to do about notification of accidents?

There is still no satisfactory answer to the first of those questions. Soviet officials have never adequately explained why they waited so long to make public notification of the accident. They have said that there was not an adequate appreciation of the seriousness of the disaster, but that hardly squares with the massive mobilisation that was under way within hours of the explosion. Nor does that argument hold when there are indications that Poland, at least, was given private warning of radiation dangers days before the public announcement.[3]

If no convincing explanation could be found for the delay in notification, the agency could still be then seen to act quickly to set up rules for the future. And less than five months after the first post-Chernobyl board meeting, a convention that required states to make early reports of accidents with possible international effects was opened for signatures in a ceremony that took place beneath the crystal chandeliers of the Hall of Audience in the Hofburg Palace. Government ministers and ambassadors from state after state took their turn in a queue, signing the agreement that pledged them to tell others about internationally-dangerous nuclear threats. The Soviet Union was the first state to sign.

At the same time, the officials affixed their names to a second convention that established ground rules for the provision of assistance to countries that suffer nuclear accidents. Blix said the speed with which the conventions had been prepared was unprecedented. The two conventions were presented as the product of a summer's urgent work by the agency. The adoption of the conventions and the affixing of signatures to them were used as the centre-piece of a September conference on nuclear safety that was designed to reassure the world that nuclear energy was actually safe. The speed and purpose of the IAEA member states was presented as an impressive example of international cooperation. But just how accurate was that presentation?

The idea for the two conventions had been around for a long time. As long ago as the agency's founding in 1957, there was discussion of the need for conventions, and the subject was discussed in the 1970s, too. But it was not until after the world's first media-spectacular nuclear accident, the Three Mile Island accident, that the convention proposals got a serious airing.

In 1981, the United States submitted to the IAEA Board

of Governors ideas for conventions on international co-operation in civil radiation emergencies. The Americans made it clear that they were acting in response to the events at TMI. In a memorandum to the board, the American delegation said:

> The experience at Three Mile Island . . . demonstrates that formidable technical and economic resources must be brought to bear in handling major nuclear accidents. The United States of America therefore suggests that it is timely to consider the preparation of an international convention that would provide the framework for co-operation in responding to civil radiation emergencies.[4]

The American delegation presented the board of governors with a proposal to draft conventions covering both emergency assistance and international notification of accidents. But the two conventions failed to gain the consensus support that is necessary for achieving results in the IAEA. American officials who participated in the 1981 effort said later that some Western European states felt that the liability issues such a convention would raise were too complex to be dealt with successfully. And, they said, the Soviet Union was not interested in such a convention because it felt that emergency responses were 'a national responsibility.'

The initiative for a convention did not die, however. Instead, that proposal led to the drafting of IAEA guidelines on emergency assistance and notification of nuclear accidents. Those guidelines were developed by groups of experts who met under IAEA sponsorship. Among the countries which participated in the drafting of the guidelines was the Soviet Union. So after Gorbachev made his May 14th speech, the resurrection of the conventions was easy, since most of the work to prepare them had been done long ago. And once Gorbachev made the speech, Soviet officials embraced the proposals as their own. For instance, at the June IAEA board meeting, the Soviet representative to the board of governors, Boris Semenov, held a press conference to promote what were now called Soviet proposals for improving nuclear safety. Semenov praised the other members of the IAEA for following Gorbachev's lead.

By the time of that board meeting, the staff work for a drafting conference for the conventions had already been done and a timetable for rushing through the early notification convention and a companion convention on emergency assistance were awaiting approval. The speed with which the conventions were drafted and put into effect was supposed to demonstrate political will. But disturbing questions remained.

First of all, why had the Soviet Union not complied with the pre-existing guidelines on reporting of accidents which it had helped to draft? When asked about this in a press conference in September 1986, Boris Shcherbina, the deputy prime minister who had overseen the Chernobyl emergency task force, maintained that there had been timely notification. This answer seemed to suggest that had the convention been in force at the time, the Soviets would have acted no more rapidly.

Another, even more worrying, question was whether an earlier warning of what was happening at Chernobyl would have made any difference. At another press conference after the conventions were opened for signature, Blix was asked that question. He said that if there had been earlier warning, it might have meant that some greenhouses could have been sealed, preventing a few crops from contamination. But he did not suggest that early notification would have averted any major effects of the Chernobyl disaster.

Then there was a little-noted provision of both conventions – a secrecy clause. Despite the fact that it was the secrecy that surrounded the early days of Chernobyl that fuelled public fear, both the new conventions included language that would allow a state with an accident to pass on information with a requirement that it be held in confidence. Whether or not such a confidence would be respected was problematic, but the fact that the agency was willing to enshrine such language in internationally-recognised instruments raised questions about the commitment to public information.

In the end, the conventions were just what Blix described them as: 'the common denominator that was achievable today.'

*   *   *

The agency achieved a major success in its effort to get the Soviet Union to report on the accident. The official Soviet report on the accident and the five-day-long post-accident review meeting in Vienna marked a watershed in Soviet information policy. For the most part the Soviet report was remarkably candid. And if the authors tended to put the blame for the accident on inexcusably bad operator errors rather than design deficiencies in the RBMK reactor, they also provided enough information for outside evaluators to judge the validity of that claim. Among the experts who participated in discussions with the Soviet team, there was a general level of satisfaction at the quality and detail of the information made available. It is worth remembering that no one from the IAEA – or for that matter no non-Soviet citizen – made a detailed inspection of the damaged Chernobyl plant, interviewed any of the surviving plant operators or examined the actual control room tapes and printouts before passing that judgment. But based on the information that was supplied, the nuclear experts said they were able to satisfy themselves that Chernobyl had not blown up because of some physical phenomenon that they had all failed to take into account. The accident had been caused not by some sort of unforeseen external agency but by safety failures of an observable, preventable nature. This raised the issue of nuclear safety and the agency's role in promoting safety.

The statute of the agency mentions safety only tangentially, but there is in the IAEA a division of nuclear safety which is charged with promoting standards for operating nuclear plants, disposing of waste and all the other aspects of nuclear safety. The division has, over the years, prepared specifications and guidelines that cover everything from power plant siting to transportation of nuclear waste. Supporters of the agency have argued that this shows a commitment to safety. Detractors say that many of the standards simply codify existing practices rather than advancing the cause of safety. Both critics and supporters agree that none of the standards is mandatory for any country.

There was, however, one IAEA safety programme that could, conceivably, have averted the Chernobyl accident. That is the Operational Safety Review.

In 1982, the agency announced that it would provide to member states the services of a team of 'very experienced individuals' who could make an evaluation of how well a nuclear power plant was being operated. The object of a review would be to look at the way the plant was being operated, how work plans were made and how the plant operators cope with events that could lead to accidents.[5] The response to this new programme was not overwhelming. By the end of 1985, only seven inspection missions had been carried out. Five were to have been done in 1986. In the wake of Chernobyl, more money and manpower have been put aside for the reviews and the agency expected to perform twelve reviews in 1987, perhaps eighteen in 1988. Those reviews are done only on invitation. And even in the wake of the Chernobyl accident, the Soviet Union had not requested a review of any of its RBMKs as by early 1987.

There is another fact to consider, too. By the end of 1986, there were 394 operating nuclear power reactors in the world. The most recent IAEA figures showed an additional 157 power reactors under construction and, over and above that, 304 research reactors were operating.[6] Even at the rate of eighteen inspections a year, it would take nearly half

a century to get around to inspecting all those reactors –
assuming that no more were ever built.

IAEA safety officials argue that it isn't necessary to
inspect every plant, only to look at types of plants. But, as
the agency itself says:

> . . . the operational safety of a plant is highly dependent
> upon the people who operate it. Two units of the same
> design, but operated by different organisations, could
> have completely different performance results. . . .[7]

IAEA officials are candid in saying that the agency is not
able to act as a sort of international policeman for the
nuclear industry. In the wake of Chernobyl there was
pressure for that to change.

In late autumn 1986, a group of government experts
convened in Vienna to begin discussing the possibility of
establishing binding international safety standards. But it
was unclear just how any state could be compelled to accept
the standards. It was also unclear how an organisation like
the IAEA, with its insistence on reaching decisions on the
basis of consensus, could be expected to establish standards
that reflected anything other than the lowest common
denominator. Indeed, any move to turn the agency into an
international regulatory body was sure to bring to mind the
experience of the United States with regulation.

Since the earliest days of the post-war American nuclear
programme – when it was decided that nuclear weapons
were too dangerous to be left to the military–American
nuclear activities were controlled by the Atomic Energy
Commission. The commission made bombs, did research
on atomic power plants, promoted nuclear energy and
regulated the civilian industry. But by 1975, there were so
many lawsuits against the AEC alleging conflict of interest
in nuclear power plant issues that the structure had to be
revamped and a separate regulatory agency (the Nuclear
Regulatory Commission) was set up to license and supervise nuclear power plants and their safety standards. If the

IAEA moved toward a more active role in setting safety standards, could it be long before the agency found itself enmeshed in the same sorts of conflict of interest?[8] As a practical matter, it is hard to see how the IAEA could become a regulatory body, since regulation implies the power of enforcement. So long as the states of the world insist on their sovereignty, the power of enforcement rests with the states, not supra-national bodies like the IAEA, and it is unlikely that the member states will be willing to hand over that power in the near future.

*   *   *

If the difficulty of balancing the promotion and policing roles were not enough for the agency, it – like so many other international bodies – is also a battleground for the ideological and economic disputes that divide the world into East and West, North and South, as well as more parochial arguments between states whose quarrels are those of next-door neighbours. In the months after Chernobyl all those sorts of disputes sprang up.

The crucial battle was the one between the Soviet Union and the Western nuclear powers. The struggle was over the question of placing the blame for the Chernobyl accident.

The Western nuclear strategy was clear from early on – to argue that the Soviet nuclear programme was both different from and inferior to Western programmes. In the halls around the IAEA board room, the word went out from the French, the West Germans, the British and the Americans that the RBMK was a badly designed reactor that lacked containment and could not be licensed in the West. A French delegate said that the goal in his mind, at least, was to make sure that when people looked at the Chernobyl accident they drew the 'correct conclusions.'

The Soviet side preferred to see Chernobyl as one of a series of major technological disasters. They pointed to the American Three Mile Island accident, the American Challenger spacecraft explosion and the Union Carbide disaster in Bhopal. What linked them all, in the Soviet view, was that men had failed to deal adequately with technology. For the Soviets, the goal was to present Chernobyl as a human failure rather than a failure of Soviet design.

This was not what the West wanted for a verdict. If human fallibility were predominantly the cause of Chernobyl, then how could Western plants be safe from similar human failures?

Throughout the summer, the battle was fought out *sotto voce*. Finally, a compromise was reached: the failure was to be attributed to 'the man-machine interface', the way that the operators interacted with the technology. It was a phrase both sides could live with. The West liked it because it made it possible to argue that Chernobyl was an example of poor design: had the control system been properly designed, the operators could not have caused the havoc they did. The Soviet nuclear establishment liked the phrase because it allowed much of the blame for the disaster to be shifted from the establishment onto the plant operators. The West couldn't live with the suggestion that Chernobyl was an example of human failure while the Soviets couldn't live with the notion that Chernobyl was an example of poor technology. The 'man-machine interface' allowed them to split the difference.

Then there was the issue of containment. Had the Chernobyl reactor been built with an adequate protective structure to trap radioactive emissions? And if not, why not? The containment issue was one on which the Americans made most of the running. In background briefings they insisted that Chernobyl had no containment worthy of the name.

When, early on, Soviet IAEA Governor Boris Semenov was asked about these charges, he said that Chernobyl did have containment, though of a different sort than in the West. He explained the containment as a system of hermetically sealed boxes. But when he was asked to point out these boxes on a diagram of the Chernobyl-style RBMK reactor, he said that the containment structures weren't shown. Eventually, what emerged was that there was, indeed, containment around parts of the plant where a significant danger of radiation escape was thought possible. Around the reactor core there was only a low-pressure containment vessel because the RBMK designers had not thought a major explosion in the reactor core possible. But in other parts of the reactor system there were massive containments, much stronger than those around some Western reactors.

The Soviet containment design was different from the Western concept: their reactor designers sought to localise any radiation leakage. The idea was that by isolating a leakage, damage would be held to a minimum. The idea was a good one, but the designers failed to anticipate the type of accident that actually happened.

The Soviets maintained that no containment could have withstood the forces that were released in the Chernobyl explosion. But the Westerners continued to argue that the failure to design adequate containment was a significant difference between East and West. This issue was kept alive by members of the American delegation to the Vienna post-accident meeting, many of whom were high-level nuclear managers who did not *want* to see containment in the Chernobyl design.

While these battles were going on, other battles, over money, were shaping up, this time pitting the Third World against the developed countries. The amount of money was small – perhaps $4 million spread over two years. It was the increase the agency sought to improve its safety programmes in the wake of Chernobyl. But at the June board of governors' meeting, the two groups argued for a whole week over how the money would be found and who would pay.

Finally, there were the neighbourly arguments. There was, for instance, the fight between Luxembourg and France over the French plans to open a new power station on the border at Cattenom. Luxembourg has tried unsuccessfully for years to stop the plant. When the negotiations over the international convention on emergency assistance after a nuclear accident started, Luxembourg used the forum to argue for, if not a ban on the plant, at least some sort of guarantee that the French would assume liability for anything that might go wrong. It was a minor issue to most of the states at the IAEA meetings, but for Luxembourg, a country with a land area about the size of the heavily contaminated zone around Chernobyl, it was the most important nuclear safety issue of the year.

Eventually, a formula was found to remove that dispute from the public agenda, too. But it seemed all too clear that while the idea of turning the IAEA into a nuclear police-man might have superficial appeal, there was little more likelihood of that happening than of the United Nations becoming an effective world government.

*   *   *

When the IAEA special conference on nuclear safety opened in the Hofburg on September 24th, 1986, sup-porters of nuclear power hoped that the special meeting – culminating in the signing of the conventions on notifi-cation and assistance after nuclear accidents – would put the seal on a summer of activity that had been designed to damp down a surge of anti-nuclear sentiment that had spread across Europe.

Even before the conference opened, anti-nuclear cam-paigners had climbed to the top of the huge Ferris wheel in the Prater amusement park and hung out a banner protest-ing against atomic power. Delegates arriving at the confer-ence hall were greeted with a typically Viennese protest – confectioneries shaped in the form of nuclear power plants, served on napkins that proclaimed atomic energy a stupid way to boil water.

The conference itself got off to a rocky start, with an address of greeting from the Austrian foreign minister, Peter Jankowitsch, in which he told the delegates that

Chernobyl had shown that 'nuclear energy is unsafe in its present operations.' And Jankowitsch had worse to say:

> For us the lessons from Chernobyl are clear. The Faustian bargain of nuclear energy has been lost. It is high time to leave the path pursued in the use of nuclear energy in the past, to develop new alternative and clean sources of energy supply.[9]

Jankowitsch got a polite hearing. But his was not a popular view in the hall.

During the following three days – including night sessions – delegates trooped to the podium at the front of the elegant converted ballroom to expound to an often nearly empty hall their governments' views on nuclear power. When the turn of Third World states came, few stayed for the rhetoric, since many of those states did not have nuclear power nor would they able to influence the course of the debate. But there was more interest as, one after another, the big nuclear powers came to the microphone and spelled out their continuing commitment to nuclear energy.

Britain's energy secretary, Peter Walker, told the conference that analysis of the Chernobyl accident has shown that 'there were mistakes in design, there were mistakes in engineering and there were mistakes in management'. Those problems could be overcome, and then, nuclear energy could provide 'immense benefits for the future of the human race.'

The American energy secretary, John Herrington, was even more blunt:

> The issue is not whether we can live with nuclear power. It is how we can make nuclear power safer. There can be no doubt that we need nuclear power and that it must continue as a key component for ensuring world energy security.

The French, who make more of their electricity from nuclear power than anyone else, were similarly committed.

But it was the chief Soviet delegate, Boris Shcherbina, who gave the most ringing endorsement of all to the nuclear path. Shcherbina had just flown in from a stint at Chernobyl, where the damage and devastation of the world's worst nuclear accident was still spread across the landscape and where hundreds of thousands of lives had been disrupted or damaged by the disaster. But he still had faith in the nuclear option, he said.

> The history of mankind knew no scientific discovery with more significant consequences than penetration into the world of the atom and harnessing its energy. The scientific and technical revolution that we witness today is based to a large extent on nuclear science and technology. More than thirty years of experience of using atoms for the benefit of mankind and for meeting social and economic requirements of people is decisive evidence that the world has irrevocably entered the nuclear age. In fact, the exploitation of atomic energy has become a realistic requirement and is preconditioned by interest in the progress of human civilisation.
>
> The Soviet Union strives [so that] achievements of the modern scientific and technical revolution are faster and more completely applied to the benefit of all nations. We shall continue to develop nuclear power in our country in accordance with our plans until the year 2000.

The message was clear: there was no chance that nuclear power could be removed from the calculations of the world. The safety conference declarations made plain that what was on offer was not abolition of nuclear power but only the possibility of an improvement in its safety.

11

COUNTING THE COST

This accident is almost a 'worst case' in terms of the risks of nuclear energy.

IAEA International Nuclear
Safety Advisory Group[1]

On October 1st, 1986, at 4.45 p.m., electrical power again flowed from the Chernobyl power plant, after a hiatus of 157 days since the last reactor was shut down on April 27th. An *Izvestia* newspaper report of the restarting of the No. 1 reactor unit said that the unit had started sending power into the grids that had been sustained during the summer by increased loads on thermal power stations. 'The Chernobyl nuclear power plant is preparing for winter,' *Izvestia* reported with satisfaction. The next task, the paper said, would be to bring the second unit back on line.[2]

The paper reported that the premises of the reactor had been decontaminated and that the second unit was cleaned up, too, while work was going ahead to make the third unit – the twin to the destroyed No. 4 unit – radiologically safe. Because of the radiation hazards around the plant, though, workers at the power plant were being rotated on shifts of five days of work followed by six days off. *Izvestia* said all the operators at the plant had been given new 'skill certification tests.' According to the newspaper, even aesthetics were not overlooked: 'the blue fir trees, that were removed when work was started to liquidate the aftermath of the accident, are to be returned by spring to their customary place near the building's entrance.' Just five months after the world's worst nuclear accident, then, a semblance of normality was returning to Chernobyl, according to *Izvestia*.

It had been a wretched five months. First, there had been the accident itself, with all its horrifying consequences. There had been international opprobrium for the delay in providing information about the accident – a delay that had seemed too much like a cover-up. The battle to control the reactor core had been another horror, with the molten fuel first seeming to cool, heating again and spewing more radioactive poison into the atmosphere, then stopping almost as suddenly as it had started. The anguish of the victims of radiation sickness had seared itself into the consciousness of the world, as had the stories of selfless bravery that were the victims' legacy. And there had been the massive evacuation – a logistical challenge like mobilising and moving an army – and an incredible decontamination campaign. There were heroes and villains, martyrs and cowards, the whole panoply of human behaviour on display. The destroyed reactor had been entombed in what was called a sarcophagus. There had been the public humiliation of going to Vienna and having the design, the operating procedures – everything – pored over by 500 foreigners. The foreigners had not been willing to give the RBMKs a clean bill of health, despite modifications in operating procedures, the addition of more control rods and a plan to change the fuel in order to end the danger of a positive coefficient of reactivity. The best the foreigners would say was that while they didn't know if the modifications would be sufficient, they 'endorsed the goal' of safety for the RBMKs. But now, despite it all, Chernobyl was back in business, at least in a limited fashion.

Was the relighting of the nuclear fire inside the reactor a triumph over adversity, a proof of how much socialist society could accomplish, or a sign of desperate pressures on the Soviet economy? The answer to this question could tell much about both the domestic health of the Soviet Union and the broader question of the likelihood of real reform of the country's politico-economic structure.

*   *   *

In the short term, it was clear that the Chernobyl accident had been a costly one for the Soviet Union. Officially, the Soviets said that the accident had cost about two billion roubles, or about two billion pounds at the official exchange rate. But that figure seems drastically low, considering that the cost of a single unit of the Chernobyl station was believed to be at least 375 million roubles.[3] Other costs, including decontamination, the construction of the sarcophagus and the expenses of the military units brought in to deal with the accident, suggest that the direct costs of the accident easily reached the two billion rouble figure by the time the plant was put back into operation.

The bill for Chernobyl covered many more items. A list might include:

  – the cost of resettlement of 135,000 people including new homes, transportation and replacement of personal belongings.
  – the value of the towns of Pripyat and Chernobyl, which will remain uninhabitable for some time.
  – lost agricultural production from contaminated lands.
  – expenses of medical treatment of Chernobyl victims.
  – expense of establishing screening and monitoring programmes for the evacuees.
  – the value of lost electrical production from the Chernobyl plant.
  – lost investment in construction on the planned unit No. 5.
  – the lost productive value of the human beings who were either killed by radiation or whose lives will be shortened by it.

All told, one Western intelligence agency placed a cost estimate for Chernobyl at perhaps as high as twenty-five billion dollars, or more than seventeen billion pounds.[4] Because of the lack of a market pricing mechanism in the Soviet Union, that estimate, like any other, was open to question. But it was surely of a more correct order of magnitude than the official one.

*   *   *

One of the immediate effects of the Chernobyl disaster was power cuts throughout the European Soviet Union. Just days after the first unit at Chernobyl had been re-started, Dimitri Protsenko, the chief of the Ministry of Electrification's energy department, gave an interview in which he appealed for energy savings throughout the country.[5] He said that in order to save enough electricity during the winter, work schedules would have to be changed with some workers only reporting in at week-ends and others working staggered shifts. The interview came after the government had already imposed major consumption-cutting measures in all the fifteen republics of the country. Street lighting had already been cut and even propaganda signs were dimmed.

Protsenko acknowledged that Chernobyl was one of the major reasons for the electricity famine, along with a drought during the summer which meant that hydroelectric production would be lower than normal. To make matters even worse, three 1,000-megawatt reactors that were supposed to start producing power during the year – at Kalinin, Zaporohye and Rovno – would not be commissioned on schedule, Protsenko said.

Throughout the 1986–87 winter, Soviet electrical authorities had to struggle to keep factories working and homes lit. Their task was made even harder by the fact that all during the summer of 1986, when many thermal power plants should have been shut down for maintenance, the plants were operating to make up for the loss of electricity from Chernobyl, in a system that was already under strain when operating fully. What had happened with the Chernobyl disaster was that the thin margin between scarcity and shortage in the Soviet electrical system had been lost. No longer could a grid controller simply shut down power to a single factory in order to keep the grid running – now power was having to be shunted around the entire unified grid system just to keep a minimal level of service. The loss of production across the entire Soviet economy was impossible to calculate.

*   *   *

Economists who study the Soviet Union are generally agreed that the Soviet Union is facing an economic crisis, one that has been developing for years. In essence, the economists say that the rigid, centrally-planned economy of the country is incapable of adjusting to the demands placed upon it. The structure of Soviet management through the *nomenklatura* system in which political reliability is an important criterion for achieving economic responsibility has made things worse. And the failure of the economy to produce the goods and services that workers want has robbed the system of incentive. As an old worker's joke has it, 'They [the managers of the economy] pretend to pay us and we pretend to work.'

The lack of a developed market – that most sensitive of economic mechanisms – means that the Soviet economy does not change as rapidly as do those in capitalist countries, giving an impression of great stability. Despite that apparent stability, there are cycles, though they are not so frequent as in the Western economies. One cycle started with the end of the Second World War. Prior to the war, economic problems had been piling up, and, paradoxically, the war and its devastation allowed a new start, with renovation and introduction of new technology. But today the Soviet Union finds itself in much the same situation as it did just before the war, with falling growth rates, obsolete technology and entrenched methodology.[6]

The stagnation of the later years of the Brezhnev period masked the problem. But in the second half of the 1980s, masking no longer worked.

In mid-September of 1986, Mikhail Gorbachev stopped in the city of Krasnodar, not far from his home base of Stavropol, while he was en route back to Moscow after his summer holiday. He met with local party and government officials and delivered a speech which many Soviet analysts found remarkably blunt. He directly addressed the problem of stagnation when he told the activists that there was no more time for them to take life easy. Gorbachev said things would have to change:

> For decades, burning issues . . . have remained unresolved. On the one hand, the appearance of active, practical work was created, decisions were taken on one matter or another. And on the other hand, right then and there, at the end of the year, when the next annual plan was being drawn up, whole volumes of amendments to the resolutions already adopted were introduced. A dangerous path: we shall not take that path. And we should warn all comrades of this.[7]

This was a clear acknowledgment of the problem – a problem that Gorbachev had come into office vowing to do something about. At first, he had talked simply of economic reforms, of the need to move from the old Stalinist-style extensive growth to the new, technology-driven world of intensive growth. Indeed, the doctrine of the 'scientific-technical revolution' had become a standard line in the mouths of leading Soviet spokesmen.

Over the years, there had been attempt after attempt to reform the Soviet economy. Khrushchev had tried reform and had failed. In 1967, at the start of the Brezhnev years, there had been another reform effort and another failure. Now, it was clear to Gorbachev that his talk of reform was running into the same sort of trouble. In his Krasnodar speech, he laid the blame for that directly on the managers of the economy. He had said that a restructuring of the economy was necessary. Not everyone understood that yet. But that was not the problem, said Gorbachev.

Time has shown that there are also quite a few people who fully understand what restructuring is. But since they understand what its consequences will be, these people do not accept restructuring. It goes against the grain with them, as the saying has it.

We know these people. They are exactly those who would like to give rather less to society and take from it rather more. . . . There are such people among workers, and peasants, and management workers and workers in the apparatus. They are also to be found in our intelligentsia.

Moreover, many of them are able to adapt quickly to a changing situation. They are resourceful. Their main concern is to preserve the old, obsolete ways, to preserve their own privileges, even though this does not accord with our principles, laws, morality or with our present policies. We can see them now shouting about restructuring from all platforms and louder than anyone else, even though they are actually applying the brake to its implementation on all kinds of pretexts, including the most specious ones.

Gorbachev's speech did not receive universal approbation. At one point, he had to chide the audience into applauding him. But if anybody needed proof that something was drastically wrong with the economy, all he had to do was look out of the window at the dark Moscow streets.

In the months after Chernobyl, there was a tendency to ascribe all sorts of Soviet positions and actions to economic weakness. For instance, some leading Western economic writers argued that the real reason the Soviet Union was making such an effort to get the Reagan Administration to give up on its Strategic Defence Initiative was that the Soviet economy could not stand the strain of high-tech competition. And *The New York Times'* respected economics writer Leonard Silk argued that Gorbachev's arms control proposals were also economy-driven.[8] Some analysts argued that too much emphasis could be placed on economic problems. They pointed out that in the days before the Second World War, there had been many people who argued that Hitler would never start a war because he could not afford it.

Other Soviet economic specialists argued that the Soviet economy might be under strain but it would survive. The US Census Bureau's Albina Tretyakova Birman put it this way:

> The Soviet economy is rather stable, like a cautious player in the stock market who won't ever take any risks. He won't get rich, but he's unlikely ever to get wiped out.[9]

But was that good enough for the new men in the Kremlin? In early 1987, it seemed not.

*   *   *

In mid-October 1986, the world's attention was focused on an island in the far North Atlantic – Iceland. There, in a small two-storey white frame building on the shoreline of the capital city, Reykjavik, the two most powerful politicians in the world, Ronald Reagan and Mikhail Gorbachev, sat down to talk. It was an extraordinary setting for an extraordinary meeting.

Reykjavik is a tiny place, with a population of about 80,000 people out of a national population of under 250,000. There is something of the American West about the city, with its vast uncrowded streets, and the vacant lots that stand in the middle of the city, as if space were the last thing in the world that was in shortage. There is something, too, of the American West in the laconic nature of the Icelanders.

Then the whole apparatus of the two superpowers descended on Reykjavik and a marauding horde of 2,500 journalists, all looking for a story, stormed into the city. For reasons best known to themselves, the Soviet media experts decided that Reykjavik was the place to bring out a team of experts to talk about what were called 'The New Realities' in the USSR. Among the panel that was on offer was a quiet-spoken man of fifty-nine named Fedor Burlatsky. Hardly anyone in the West had heard of him.

Burlatsky, like many others in the top ranks of Soviet society, wears several hats. He is a political scientist – one of the people who led the fight for the recognition of political science as a separate discipline in the Soviet Union and now vice president of the Soviet Political Science Association and chief of the Department of Political Philosophy of the Academy of Social Science. He is a high-ranking member of the *nomenklatura*, a former chief of the Communist Party Central Committee's Department of Socialist Countries, and he is a political commentator for the influential journal *Literaturnaya Gazeta*. He numbers among his friends the well-known specialist on the United States, Georgi Arbatov, and Foreign Ministry Press spokesman Gennadi Gerasamov. He was at one time a speech writer for Nikita Khrushchev, and he is a long-time associate of the man at the top of the Soviet Union, Mikhail Gorbachev.

After the panel discussion, Burlatsky agreed to sit down privately with three journalists and talk about what was going on in the Soviet Union. His remarks were stunning in their frankness.

In his earlier public remarks, Burlatsky had acknowledged the need to restructure Soviet management. The journalists asked if this meant that Gorbachev was planning a change in the way that managers were selected so that management skills became more important and political qualifications less so.

Burlatsky's answer was simple: yes. But he didn't stop there. The policy of the Soviet Union was that there had to be an infusion of democracy in order to make the economy work: without democratisation, there could be no meaningful economic reforms. Did this mean that Gorbachev was going to take on the *nomenklatura*? Burlatsky was temporarily bemused:

> I don't remember that Gorbachev used this term *nomenklatura*, but the economic and social reforms, the reforms in the political sphere, need new men, new people. This is a very old story, that new policies need new people. Therefore, as you can see, there are many changes at high political level. . . . Now may be the time for the second level, for the management in the economic sphere [and] in the different social organisations.[10]

The journalists were taken aback by what Burlatsky was saying. One of them asked, did he mean to suggest that reforms were needed because the Soviet Union was not democratic enough? Burlatsky said that this was a theoretical question. But, he added, it was also a practical question:

> . . . because [before now] we usually used the term 'the further development of democracy' [to describe what was needed]. But now, it is not enough. [You must] understand that we need a very big step and a very deep process in democracy in different fields. We need it. . . . This is, I repeat, a precondition for our success in economic and social spheres.

The way ahead was through using the already existing provisions of Soviet law to achieve democracy and through the creation of new institutions that would allow workers to have a real say in how the society was run. In addition, the role of the press and public opinion would have to be dramatically revamped so that 'writers, scientists and other active people' could 'take part in discussions about important government decisions.'

This was not the sort of conversation the journalists were used to from such a senior member of the Soviet establishment. One asked if this new thrust in internal policy had anything to do with relations with the United States. Burlatsky said yes, that if the Soviet Union could get some agreements with the United States then it could use the saved expenditure 'for our peace economy.' But that was not the real reason for the push:

> The main reason is [the need] for reforms. We want . . . the new technology and to take part in the new techno-logical revolution. We want to be on a high level in all fields. This is the main problem, and therefore there are very close connections between our internal process of reform and democratisation and our relations with the West.

Burlatsky said that among the reforms that he expected to see emerging in the Soviet Union were more scope for individual activity – a jargon phrase for a form of private enterprise – and for more self-management in factories and less interference from above. He said that it would be possible to compare some of what Gorbachev had in mind to the speeches of the Chinese and Hungarians – two of the least orthodox members of the Communist community.

What would happen to the Communist Party itself under this new vision? After all, the party is supposed to exercise the leading role in society. Well, Burlatsky said, the party would deal with strategic planning, about creating new conditions for social and political organisations. The party would have to go out and find the new people to run the country, too – people who were 'more active, more talented, more educated,' but still socialists. The party would not, however, be doing 'what they were doing during a long time – not to decide the concrete problems.'

As the days of the Reykjavik meeting wore on, the journalists who had participated in the interview crossed paths occasionally. They were all fascinated by what Burlatsky had said. To be sure, Gorbachev had used the term 'democratisation' in his Krasnodar speech. But that seemed to legitimise further Burlatsky's comments rather than to detract from them.

If Burlatsky were to be believed – if Gorbachev himself were to be believed – the new leaders of the Soviet Union had decided to take on the *nomenklatura*.

There were reasons for scepticism. Was it possible that the campaign for democratisation was nothing more than a means to strike at the old guard officials in the party and the government who owed no loyalty to Gorbachev and company? Historically minded analysts could point to pledges of collective leadership that previous Soviet leaders had offered upon taking office, pledges that were forgotten after the new leader had managed to gain control of the levers of power. But the campaign for reform and democratisation was different – for one thing, it was being waged publicly, on the screens of Soviet television. And it wasn't just power sharing in the party leadership that was being proposed, but increased power to the Soviet people.

Even the way in which the Chernobyl accident had been reported domestically – in detail that was considered nothing short of revolutionary by long-time readers of the Soviet press – made it clear that a new game was afoot.

Another hint that Gorbachev might be serious were the rumours that went around Moscow in early autumn that he had been the target of an assassination attempt. The Soviet media were far from open enough to report on such an event, let alone to mention rumours, but two schools of thought emerged.

The first was simply that they were true, that Gorbachev had been the target of an assassin, possibly put up to the task by some threatened faction. The second theory was that the rumours were manufactured to undermine Gorbachev's authority. It was all very puzzling.

*   *   *

One of the most fascinating questions to arise out of Chernobyl was what it would mean for Mikhail Gorbachev. Chernobyl was for him – master political operative – both a danger and an opportunity. It was a danger because of the crippling effect the Chernobyl disaster – coupled with other energy problems – was having on the Soviet economy. Chernobyl could not bring Gorbachev down, but it could be used as a weapon by his opponents inside the party and the government. But Chernobyl was also an opportunity: if Gorbachev could pull it off, he could present the triumph over disaster as his new regime's own, while pointing the finger of blame for Chernobyl at entrenched obstructionists in the *nomenklatura*.

The challenge for Gorbachev was to use Chernobyl for his own ends rather than allowing himself to be dragged down by it. Watching him cope would be a fascinating political drama, but one with the most momentous implications for the rest of the world.

In late 1986, Gorbachev was signalling that he was going on the offensive. In Reykjavik where he met Reagan, both he and his supporters went out of their way to spell out their desire to end the arms race as a means of doing something about domestic economic problems. And in speeches clearly aimed at domestic audiences, Gorbachev served notice that he wanted to make fundamental changes in the way the Soviet Union operated.

In Iceland, Gorbachev had shown himself a high-stakes strategic player. In his past career, he had also demonstrated an ability to land on his feet. He had managed to take on the chronically disastrous field of agriculture and to escape with his reputation not only intact but enhanced. After what seemed to be a rebuff from the leadership when he tried to succeed Andropov and lost to Chernenko, he had a year later taken the top prize with aplomb. He had managed to convince Andrei Gromyko to back his candidacy, only to remove Gromyko from power with an elevation to the presidency.

The electric power crisis that Chernobyl had triggered in the Soviet Union was a real challenge to the new leaders in the Kremlin. As the Soviet Union prepared to move into winter, Gorbachev was faced with the reality that the winter of 1986–87 would be a Soviet 'Winter of Discontent.' There would be too little electrical power to go around; workers would have to turn out for shifts at odd hours, stumbling through ill-lit streets in blizzards to reach factories that might themselves be chilly.

With oil prices still far below those when he took office, Gorbachev and the economic planners were forced to take tough decisions. One of those decisions was apparently to cut back on imports of consumer goods. By December, coffee had become a scarcity item because the country could not spare the hard currency to buy it. There were even some suggestions that the Soviet Union would have to go to the international financial markets for a loan.

One needed only to think back to the British 'Winter of Discontent' of 1973–74 in which power cuts were instrumental in bringing down the government of Edward Heath to understand how potentially devastating dark factories and offices could be. Of course, Gorbachev couldn't be voted out of office in the same way, but the Soviet Union was no longer a society in which the people could always be counted on to remain docile, a fact that was underscored when the capital city of the Soviet republic of Kazakhstan, Alma-Ata, erupted in nationalist riots in December.

The rioting had been touched off after Gorbachev removed the Kazakh party chief, Dinkmukhamed Kunayev, an old-style *nomenklaturist* who had flourished under Leonid Brezhnev's corrupt and easy-going regime. The rioters were not, apparently, so much angered at Kunayev's dismissal as they were by his replacement, an ethnic Russian who was being sent in to shape up the republic along the new Gorbachev lines. Kunayev's forced removal was followed almost immediately by harsh criticism of Brezhnev in an article in *Pravda*. The article, which was published to mark the anniversary of the late leader's death, blamed Brezhnev for many of the economic troubles besetting the country.

Developments like these made it clear that Gorbachev was actually committed to taking on the *nomenklatura*: the challenge was to turn the discontent with the way things were in the Soviet Union into a weapon to use against the old-line bureaucrats of the *nomenklatura* rather than to let the *nomenklatura* use the discontent to oust him.

*   *   *

The Chernobyl nuclear disaster came at a crucial time in the history of the Soviet Union, at a moment when a fundamental debate had already started about the role of the state and party, about the relationship of governors and governed, about the basic legitimacy of Soviet society.

The man who was the symbol of the debate, Mikhail Gorbachev, had stood on Lenin's Tomb just six days after Chernobyl erupted and smiled and waved to the marchers below as if he had not a care in the world. But Gorbachev, the best educated Soviet leader since Lenin, knew too well that while he might have emerged as the leader of one of the world's two superpowers, he was the leader, too, of a society that had failed, in spectacular fashion, to live up to its self-professed goals.

The Soviet Union had promised an advanced industrial state, but from consumer goods to the nuclear industry, the controlled press had reported a litany of failures that would have sounded like anti-Soviet propaganda if it had come from any other source. Gorbachev was well aware that after seventy years of extensive industrialisation, the Soviet Union still relied, like an underdeveloped country, on the export of raw materials – oil and gas – for the biggest share of its hard currency earnings. In a state that took as its justification the benefit of the workers, the workers themselves were ill-housed, still stood in queues for food, and drank so much that an official campaign had to be launched to attack the rampant alcoholism that scarred Soviet life. It was a society that was so frightened of criticism that it had locked its critics in jail, and had refused to allow its citizens who wished to do so the right to leave.

What Chernobyl showed, in a graphic form, was that the Soviet Union had not only failed in its goals of improvement, but it had actually done harm to its people. And then, for days, it had kept silent, refusing to reveal what had happened.

When information about what had happened at Chernobyl was made public, the Soviet report described the accident as the equivalent of pilot error, a disaster caused by a few technicians who, through ineptness and incompetence, had managed to destroy an otherwise excellent reactor, just as an aeroplane pilot might fly an excellent aircraft into the side of a mountain.

The truth was, if anything, worse than the explanation that a few individuals could casually manage to send thousands of people to early graves by mistakenly flipping a few switches. Reading between the lines of the Soviet report, Western nuclear experts discovered that the Chernobyl disaster was the fault of a basic design flaw in the reactor that allowed a 'prompt reactivity excursion,' a slow-motion nuclear explosion, to take place inside the reactor. It was a fundamental error, and one that the designers of the RBMK reactor knew was incorporated in the design. But the design had become one of two standard Soviet reactor types because it was cheap and easy to build. The RBMK had been designed as it was for economic reasons, and safety had been a secondary consideration.

There was also evidence that the Soviet Union had advance warning of operational problems with the RBMK: a little-noted comment in the official accident report hinted that as early as 1980, in Kursk, another RBMK had suffered a severe accident. The international panel of experts who reviewed the Soviet report said, in the dry language of technical writing, that:

> The events at the Kursk station . . . would be extremely interesting for examining some of the important transient [accident] characteristics of the Chernobyl station.

By late 1986, that interest remained unsatisfied.

The accident revealed other major inadequacies, too. If intelligence reports are to be believed, as many as 200 people from the nearby town of Pripyat were allowed to drive out to the plant site to watch the fire, at the time when the reactor was at its most deadly, spewing forth massive doses of radiation. And control room operators at the Nos. 1 and 2 reactor units were kept on duty for more than twenty-four hours to keep those two units running at the height of the nuclear release, while it was unclear whether the fire inside the No. 4 reactor could even be brought under control. The power plant site itself was flooded with up to one million gallons of radioactive water that was ineffectively pumped over the reactor.

The evacuation of Pripyat, thirty-six hours after the start of the disaster and after hours of high radioactive discharges, revealed the woefully inadequate preparations that the authorities had made – or failed to make – for an elementary part of any nuclear safety programme. Not until May 2nd did the authorities evacuate Chernobyl town and then only after a visit to the area by Soviet Prime Minister Nikolai Ryzhkov. Privately, some Western nuclear experts said that inadequate though it might have been, the Soviet Union probably did a better job of getting its citizens out of harm's way than their own countries could in similar circumstances.

Where the Soviet system did come into its own was in the lumbering, but ultimately effective way that the entire resources of the state were concentrated on the disaster.

Helicopter pilots and chemical warfare troops were drafted in, as well as raw materials for the struggle.

The Soviet media compared the struggle at Chernobyl to battles in the Second World War. It turned out that the comparison was more apt than might have been thought, when an Estonian newspaper reporter revealed that there were unwilling conscripts in the battle of Chernobyl, Estonian reservists who were forced to do decontamination work for up to six months, men who called themselves 'heroes against our will.'

The encasement of the destroyed reactor in its concrete and metal tomb was called by outside experts a 'major technical innovation', but the experts were worried about how long the tomb could be expected to protect the environment from the virulent radiation it encased. Some of the radioactive elements in the reactor had half-lives of hundreds or thousands of years, but the experts thought the tomb might be safe for no more than fifty years.

Then there was the haste to return Chernobyl to power production. By October, the Soviet press was reporting that the first unit had been returned to service – but at what cost?

The operators who would control the station would have to pass through a zone of contamination every time they entered or left the plant. And because of the radiation to which they would be exposed, they could only work for five days at a time, followed by a six-day layoff. It was hard to imagine that such stressful conditions were an ideal environment for critically important work.

*　　　*　　　*

If the Soviet Union came off badly in the Chernobyl disaster, so did almost everyone else.

In the days after the accident, a Western press that was denied access to one of the biggest stories of the decade failed to live up to basic standards of responsibility. There were screaming headlines tolling deaths in the thousands and reports that the Chernobyl reactor had completely melted down. There were stories of panics in the Soviet Union that never actually occurred. But official Soviet complaints about the Western reporting conveniently failed to mention that in their own way, the Soviet media were even more irresponsible because they failed to warn the people who depended upon them about the invisible dangers to which they were being exposed.

In Eastern Europe, there was a general tendency to play down the danger from Chernobyl, though the Polish government did move quickly to protect Polish children from the danger of radioactive iodine with special medication. But in the months after the disaster, there was a growing awareness among Eastern Europeans that their governments had been too cavalier in their attitude toward the Chernobyl menace and indeed toward nuclear energy in general. The long-term effect of the Chernobyl disaster on the psyche of Eastern Europeans might be as profound as the Prague Spring and the subsequent Warsaw Pact invasion of Czechoslovakia in 1968. Could Chernobyl become the key to a real radicalisation of significant numbers of young people in countries like Poland, Czechoslovakia and Hungary?

If Eastern European governments reacted too little, Western Europeans reacted wildly and often irrationally. Ill-considered food import bans and exemptions made a shambles of any pretence that there were commonly agreed standards for radiation safety and exposed Western governments to the charge that they were using the fear of contamination for commercial advantage. Countries with big nuclear power programmes, like Britain and France, tended to play down dangers, although in Britain, some sheep were still banned for sale to the public as too radioactive even in December 1986.

One bizarre reaction to Chernobyl was that of many anti-nuclear activists in Western European countries: when Chernobyl blew up, they focused their concern not on the demonstrated dangers of the Soviet nuclear programme

but on the demand for the closure of some specific plant in
their own countries. Despite the fact that the nuclear
plumes from Chernobyl had spread all across Western
Europe, there was not so much as a peep of protest when
Chernobyl No. 1 was started up again. Had the same
sequence of events taken place in any Western country,
there would have been no way for a government that
permitted it to remain in office.

Just as odd was the fact that for the most part the Western
anti-nuclear groups tended to focus only on plants in their
own countries, for the most part ignoring the plants
in neighbouring states. British activists' demands for a
shut-down of Sellafield seemed oddly insular when one
considered that just across the English Channel, in
Gravelines, between Calais and Dunkerque, was a bigger
concentration of nuclear power reactors than any in
Britain.

And what of the supporters of nuclear power?

Western nuclear interests were torn between two conflicting goals – to attack the Soviet nuclear programme as
being incomparably worse than anything that would be
allowed in the West and, on the other hand, telling people
that radiation was not the danger that anti-nuclear activists
and some quite reputable radiation biologists insisted it
was. On more than one occasion, this led to the same
individual publicly insisting that the accident was being
overplayed by the press, while privately telling journalists
that he had known for years that the RBMK was an unsafe
reactor. The unasked question hung in the air: if this were
known, why had no warnings been given?

The response of the International Atomic Energy
Agency – two conventions that set up rules for reacting to
nuclear accidents and a modest increase in spending on
nuclear safety (an amount about equivalent to one per cent
of the cost of a single nuclear power plant) – was in fact an
example of the lowest common denominator response of an
agency that operates in secret and on the basis of
consensus.

The agency's only successes were the post-accident review meeting and the follow-up study done by the International Safety Advisory Group. But even in those efforts,
the agency was reduced to working with secondary sources:
copies of computer print-outs and computer tapes were not
provided for the international experts, nor were on-site
technical inspections allowed. The only IAEA officials who
actually visited Chernobyl during the period of acute crisis
were Director General Hans Blix, who is not a scientist,
and his deputies Leonard Konstantinov and Morris Rosen.
Their visit was limited to a helicopter flight over the site.
Confronted with a superpower which did not want too
much scrutiny, the agency showed itself all too compliant.
The performance of the agency in the Chernobyl crisis
underlined the powerlessness of the only world-wide nuclear organisation with responsibility for nuclear safety.
And it showed what an opportunity had been missed when
the chance to internationalise atomic energy was lost in the
days after the Second World War.

*   *   *

Chernobyl was not, however, just some sort of political
morality play, acted out for a watching audience. The
disaster at Chernobyl touched a raw nerve in horrified
onlookers, a sense that something was badly wrong in the
world.

Many thoughtful people saw Chernobyl as a symbol of a
world gone awry – a world in which technology was out of
control. The list of disasters was a long one: the catastrophe
of Bhopal, the ruin of Times Beach, Missouri, in America
through dioxin pollution, the tragedy of Japan's mercury
poisoned children, the wastage of Vietnam by Agent
Orange, the devastation of Kyshtym, the horrifying spectacle of the explosion of Challenger, the destruction of the
Black Forest by acid rain . . . a roll call that could go on for
pages.

Now, with Chernobyl there was a real demonstration of

the dangers nuclear plants could pose. It was no wonder that there were calls for the abolition of nuclear power. Being anti-nuclear no longer seemed out of the mainstream of public opinion.

Other well-meaning and intelligent people, like the IAEA's director of nuclear safety, Morris Rosen, a man of unquestioned integrity, argued that Chernobyl, for all its horror, was preferable to the alternative – reverting to a world in which the requirement for electrical power was met by burning fossil fuels. Energy economists asked just where the generating capacity would be found to replace the more than 270,000 megawatts of electricity that nuclear power provided to an energy-hungry world.

There were charts and graphs in profusion to demonstrate that burning the amount of coal that would be needed to replace nuclear power would bring on many more premature deaths than had Chernobyl. Londoners of a certain age could remember back to the days after the war when killer smog claimed thousands of lives. The experts pointed out that coal power plants actually put radiation into the air, too, radiation that was found in the coal itself.

As for oil, the price of petroleum might be down now, but a big return to burning oil would soon end the OPEC oil glut and allow prices to pass anything ever paid before. That was a problem for people besides the money men: when oil prices rise, so do all energy prices. Higher fuel prices mean that people on low incomes get cold when winter comes and sometimes freeze to death, hardly the sort of outcome the anti-nuclear forces would wish.

But what about alternative sources of energy?

In the 1970s, solar power, wind power and hydroelectric power were held out as the salvation that would soon arrive. To date, the millennium has not yet come. One symbol of the failure might be the big power-generating windmill that the American National Aeronautics and Space Administration erected out on the American High Plains in Clayton, New Mexico, one of the windiest places in the United States.

For years, the windmill was a landmark, something that drivers could see from a distance. But after NASA finished its experiment with the windmill, it was declared surplus and offered to the town of Clayton, to use for 'free' electricity. The city fathers turned it down as not cost effective. The windmill is now gone.

Solar power, too, has not developed yet into a technology that offers a real chance of replacing conventional or nuclear power. The cost of solar cells is still too high, and the problem of storing electricity for the dark hours at a reasonable cost has not yet been tackled.

That leaves hydroelectricity, and there, too, the record does not promote hope. For one thing, many of the best hydroelectric sites have been developed already. There is a finite number of spots where dams can be built at a reasonable cost. And despite the claims that hydroelectric power is environmentally benign, try telling that to anyone who has lived downstream of a broken dam.

At least windmills, solar power and hydroelectricity exist. But there was another form of alternative energy – fusion, a technology that would replicate in miniature the energy of the sun. Fusion power would be, its supporters said, the ultimate solution. The problem was, that after decades of research and massive expenditures, no one had yet managed to make it work, though there were continuing promises that it would soon be possible to produce a fusion reaction that would generate more energy than it consumed. But, just as it had been for so long, the timetable for that reaction was still 'five years more.'

The point is, of course, that we have built a world in which energy is the key. So much of our lifestyle, everything from our Walkman tape players, to our synthetic-fibre clothes, to the food we eat, to the medicines that keep us healthy, depends on big inputs of energy. The consumption of energy is itself a measure of the level of civilisation, according to some economists. There are few of us who would be willing to alter radically our living standards or life styles in order to make the cuts that breaking the dependence on energy would require.

In that sense, Austrian Foreign Minister Peter Janko-witsch was right when he referred to the 'Faustian bargain of nuclear energy.' But when he argued that other states could opt out of nuclear energy with the same ease that his country had done, he was ignoring the larger reality around him. And it is not likely that Jankowitsch or even the most ardent nuclear power opponent would wish to see Austria's forests despoiled by more acid rain from fossil fuel power plants. The question posed by Chernobyl is whether we so value our energy-intensive lifestyle that we are willing to take the risks that it imposes as its price; whether we are willing to take those risks for our children and all the generations yet unborn. And if not, just what *are* we willing to give up? Based on the evidence to date, the answer appears to be: nothing.

* * *

Nuclear power may be a Faustian bargain, but for now it is a bargain that modern industrial society seems destined to keep. If nuclear power is here to stay, at least for some decades more, the question to ask is: was Chernobyl really the worst case? The evidence is mixed.

Experts on the technical details of nuclear accidents – including one man who has made a life's work out of trying to blow up reactors in the interest of making them safer and who spoke to the authors privately – seem to think that from a technical point of view that assessment may be correct.

The expert view holds that there are physical and chemical reasons why even with a core meltdown of a reactor, the resulting disaster might be self-limiting.

But what about the China Syndrome, in which molten fuel burns its way down to the water table, then sets off hydrogen explosions?

While that might happen, the experts point out that the molten fuel would not simply go straight down, but it would tend to spread out. It is far from clear that the fuel would escape from the structure or that it would stay concentrated enough to do the damage that the China Syndrome proposes.

So perhaps Chernobyl is a worst case in that sense. But there were four 'What ifs' that made it clear that Chernobyl could have been much worse.

First, what if the firemen had not been willing to lay down their lives to put out the blaze? Given the design of Chernobyl – one reactor after another strung out in shotgun fashion along a nearly half-mile long building – what would have happened if the blaze had spread to the No. 3 unit, then on to Nos 1 and 2? Given the fact that the plant authorities did not order an immediate shutdown of the other reactors, the potential was there for the other reactor control rooms to be engulfed by fire even while the reactors were running. Or control cables could have caught on fire, perhaps knocking out safety controls. If the inadequately equipped, largely unprotected fire crews had not so heroically tackled the fire with the near-certain knowledge that they faced death, would Chernobyl have been confined to a one-reactor disaster?

The second question is what if the bombardment of the reactor with boron carbide, sand, clay, and lead had not been devised, apparently on the spur of the moment?

The initial attempt to control the reactor core with water was a failure. All that effort did was to produce huge quantities of radioactive water that nearly flooded other reactor units. If the reactor had not been capped, how much more of the inventory of highly radioactive elements would have been released into the air? How many more people might face early cancers? How many more mothers might wonder about their babies' chances for a normal life? How much worse would be the damage to the environment?

The third question is what if the plume of radioactivity had not been lofted so high into the atmosphere and so widely dispersed? If, instead, the total amount of radioactivity released in just the first day had settled on, say, Kiev, who knows what sort of story Chernobyl might have turned out to be?

But it is the fourth question that is the most frightening: what if the RBMK that blew up had not been out in the lightly populated Pripyat Marshes but had been one of the RBMKs outside Leningrad, or perhaps at Ignalina, in Lithuania. Ignalina is itself not a big city, but Lithuania is much more densely populated than is the Pripyat region. And Leningrad is a city of more than 4.6 million people. The difficulty of getting 135,000 people out of the way of nuclear disaster gives little hope if a similar accident were to take place near a big metropolitan area.

Chernobyl may be close to the worst case that a nuclear power plant accident can produce as far as the physical and chemical reactions are concerned. But it is clear that had the accident developed differently or had it happened in a different location, the damage, destruction and death that would have resulted would have been much higher. What is not in doubt is that there will be more Chernobyls: even the staunchest defenders of nuclear power accept that there will be nuclear accidents, some with horrific consequences. It may be, as sincere and dedicated nuclear engineers maintain, that the worst that nuclear power can do is less of a danger than that posed by the alternatives. But that verdict is, at best, unproved.

AFTERWORD

In January, 1987, the Soviet physicist who directed the operation to build the sarcophagus around Chernobyl Unit No. 4, Academician Yevgeny Velikhov, went to Washington where he discussed the clean-up operation with members of the United States Senate Committee on Labour and Human Resources. Velikhov told the committee that he was worried about the spring rains in the Ukraine – rains that would raise the water flow from the marshlands around the Chernobyl plant by up to ten times. The higher water flows could wash radioactive contamination into the Pripyat and Dnieper rivers.

The spring rains would be a new trial after one of the harshest winters the Soviet Union had ever endured. Intense cold put heavy strains on the power system and made the rush to return Chernobyl to electricity production understandable. Even with the country's generators, gas pipelines and coal trains working flat out, there were days when whole areas of Soviet cities went without heat when district heating plants failed.

The Soviet Union continued to restrict access to the Chernobyl region, allowing only carefully-selected foreigners in for short visits. The first foreign government official to tour the wrecked plant was British Energy Secretary Peter Walker in mid-December. In January, IAEA Director-General Hans Blix returned from a brief visit to Chernobyl. Blix reported that he was told that life was slowly returning to normal around the plant. But Academician Velikhov was quoted as saying that contamination within the 19-mile exclusion zone remained quite high. He would not predict when the evacuees could return home.

Chernobyl had focused the attention of the world on the need for better nuclear safety measures. But the accident did not stop the trend to nuclear power. In January, 1987, the IAEA reported that in no country did the accident lead to a halt in the construction or putting into operation of a nuclear power plant. The two conventions on international response to nuclear accidents which were the centrepiece of the IAEA's post-Chernobyl nuclear safety response went into force. But by late January, only Norway, the Soviet Union and the Soviet republics of Byelorussia and the Ukraine had ratified the convention on emergency assistance.

Chernobyl offered numerous lessons. Mikhail Gorbachev seemed to have learned many of them. He continued to use the nuclear catastrophe as an example of the failings of Soviet industrial society and of the pressing need for profound changes in the way his country was managed and governed. In a January, 1987, speech he made the link explicit:

> In recent years there has been a noticeable increase in the economic growth rates after setting things in order and dealing with carelessness. Yet this task remains urgent. Loose discipline and a lowering of responsibility are too deeply rooted and are felt painfully to this day. It is precisely criminal irresponsibility and carelessness, which are the main causes of such tragic events as the accident at the Chernobyl nuclear power plant . . .

Chernobyl was the most explicit demonstration possible of how urgent Gorbachev's task of 'setting things in order' in the Soviet Union had become.

NOTES

1 May Day/Mayday

1 Kiev domestic service in Ukrainian at 2.15 GMT, May 2nd, 1986.

2 This chapter was compiled from *Reuter*, *Associated Press*, and *United Press International* reports from Moscow on May 1st, 1986. Various Soviet media reports were also used.

3 See Hedrick Smith, *The Russians*, Sphere Books, London, 1976, for a summary of the significance of the May Day parades, pp. 334–368.

4 See Michael Binyon, *Life in Russia*, Panther Books, London, 1985, pp. 168–170, for a discussion of the May Day ceremonies and the role of propaganda in the Soviet Union.

5 The forty slogans of the CPSU Central Committee for May Day, 1986, were published by *Pravda*, April 13th, 1986.

6 *Pravda*, June 15th, 1986.

7 *Pravda*, May 21st, 1986.

8 From a *Vremya* newscast on the Moscow Television Service 14.30 GMT, May 2nd, 1986.

9 The information in this section, except where otherwise attributed, is drawn from Western and Soviet newspapers and news agencies. Most of the reports were published on May Day or within a few days of May Day.

10 Private comment of a scientist attending a meeting of World Health Organisation experts at Bilthoven, Netherlands, June 25th–27th, 1986. The meeting was called to discuss Chernobyl. The scientist spoke on condition he was not identified.

11 See 'Information Policy and other Measures,' in a report prepared for the Rainbow Group in the European Parliament, Brussels, 1986.

12 Blix's comment at the International Atomic Energy Agency in Vienna was widely quoted.

13 See *Tass* correspondent A. Lyuty, 'Those people in the United States who stand to gain from organising a hysterical spectacle around the accident at Chernobyl,' *Sovetskaya Rossiya*, May 8th, 1986, p. 3.

14 From *What Happened And What Is To Be Done*, a cyclostyled information sheet published in Poland by the underground organisation *Kos* on May 4th, 1986.

2 The Secret Disaster

1 Quoted by William J. Eaton, 'Soviet stonewalling on Chernobyl seen as an attempt to avoid panic,' *Los Angeles Times*, June 19th, 1986.

2 Quoted by Eaton, op. cit.

3 See Harrison Salisbury, 'Gorbachev's Dilemma,' *The New York Times Magazine*, July 27th, 1986.

4 See text of Gorbachev's national television address, *Pravda*, May 15th, 1986, p. 1.

5 See Marshall I. Goldman, 'Gorbachev openness goes up in smoke,' *Los Angeles Times*, June 18th, 1986.

6 Goldman, op. cit.

7 Quoted in Robert Gillette, 'Evidence mounts that Kremlin quickly knew of Chernobyl,' *Los Angeles Times*, July 20th, 1986.

8 Gillette, op. cit.

9 Gillette, op. cit.

10 Gillette, op. cit.

11 Gillette, op. cit.

12 See Eaton in *Los Angeles Times*, op. cit.

13 Gillette, op. cit.

14 See Thomas Powers, 'Chernobyl as a paradigm of a Faustian bargain,' *Discover*, June 1986. The authors have used a number of examples of Soviet secrecy from the Powers article.

15 See Martin McCauley, *Stalin and Stalinism*, Longman, London, 1983, pp. 85–86.

16 David K. Shipler, *Russia: Broken Idols, Solemn Dreams*, Futura, London, 1985, p. 214.

17 Powers, op. cit.

18 Quoted by Henrik Bering-Jensen, 'How the Soviets Break News: Selectively and Dishonestly,' *Insight* magazine, June 2nd, 1986.

19 Powers, op. cit.
20 For a concise discussion of the basics of the Czarist system see David Lane, *State and Politics in the USSR*, Blackwell, Oxford, 1985.
21 V. I. Lenin, *What is to Be Done?*, Foreign Languages Publishing House, Moscow, 1951, p. 19.
22 Lenin, *What is to Be Done?*, p. 20.
23 The details on the radio listening habits of Soviet leaders are from an article titled 'Where the Kremlin gets the news, and how,' by Vladimir Solovyov and Elena Klepikova, which was published in *The Christian Science Monitor*, June 19th, 1986.

3 Stalin's Legacy

1 Mikhail Gorbachev, address to Party workers in Tyumen Oblast, reported in BBC *Summary of World Broadcasts* translation of the broadcast of the speech as carried by Soviet television, cited as *SWB 9th Sep. 1985 USSR: Conference of Tyumen and Tomsk Oblast Economic Activists*.
2 These percentages are derived from official Soviet figures and are cited by David Lane and Felicity O'Dell in *The Soviet Industrial Worker: Social Class, Education and Control*, Martin Robertson, London, 1978, pp. 7–11.
3 Lenin, *What Is To Be Done?*, op. cit., p. 225.
4 V. I. Lenin, quoted by Ronald J. Hill in *Soviet Union: Politics, Economics and Society*, Francis Pinter (Publishers) Ltd, London, 1985, p. 117.
5 Gavrill Popov, *Management of Socialist Production*, Progress Publishers, Moscow, 1986. All quotations from Popov are from this source.
6 *Lektsii po Partiinomu Stroitel'stvu*, Mysl', Moscow, 1971, quoted by Leslie Holmes, *Politics in the Communist World*, Oxford University Press, Oxford, 1986, p. 135.
7 Michael Voslensky, *Nomenklatura: Anatomy of the Soviet Ruling Class*, tr. by Eric Mosbacher, The Bodley Head, London, 1984, p. 95.
8 Michael Binyon, *Life in Russia*, Panther Books, Granada Publishing Ltd, London, 1983, p. 25. Chapter One, 'The Tyranny of the Plan,' is particularly illuminating and useful.
9 Binyon, op. cit., pp. 25–26.
10 See Gary Taubes and Glenn Garelik, 'Soviet Science: How

good is it?' in *Discover* magazine, August 1986. This is an excellent article and the authors have borrowed extensively from it.

11 Taubes and Garelik, op. cit.

12 See Geoffrey Hosking, *A History of the Soviet Union*, Fontana, London, 1985, for a useful guide to Stalin's industrialisation programme.

13 Lionel Kochan and Richard Abraham, *The Making of Modern Russia*, Penguin Books, London, 1983, p. 368.

14 Kochan and Abraham, op. cit., p. 374.

15 Hedrick Smith, *The Russians*, Sphere, London, 1979, p. 282n.

16 Binyon, op. cit., p. 239.

17 Marshall Goldman, *Environmental Pollution in the Soviet Union*, MIT Press, Cambridge, Massachusetts, and London, 1972, p. 220.

18 See Frank Furedi, *The Soviet Union Demystified: a Materialist Analysis*, Junius Publications Ltd, London, 1986, for an examination of Stalin's drive for industrialisation by an unsympathetic Marxist scholar.

19 The text of Gorbachev's Tyumen speech was carried in Soviet newspapers. However, some of his remarks were omitted. The version used here is from the BBC *Summary of World Broadcasts* translation of the broadcast of the speech as carried on Soviet television and is cited as *SWB 9th Sep. 1985 USSR: Conference of Tyumen and Tomsk Oblast Economic Activists*.

20 Much of the information about Soviet oil reserves and earnings in this section comes from the American Central Intelligence Agency's *USSR Energy Atlas*, Washington, 1985.

21 Albina Tretyakova and Meredith Heinemeier, *Cost estimates of the Soviet coal industry: 1970 to 1990*, CIR Staff paper No. 18, Centre for International Research, US Bureau of the Census, Washington, 1986, p. 3.

22 Albina Tretyakova and Meredith Heinemeier, *Cost estimates of the Soviet oil industry: 1970 to 1990*, CIR Staff paper No. 20, Centre for International Research, US Bureau of the Census, Washington, 1986, p. 1.

23 W. P. Geddes, *Nuclear Power in the Soviet Bloc*, The Uranium Institute, London, 1984.

24 Remarks made in private conversation, August 1986.

25 *Financial Times*, London, April 18th, 1985.

4 The Nuclear Economy

1 Quoted in Robert Jungk, *Brighter than a Thousand Suns: A Personal History of the Atomic Scientists*, Harcourt Brace Jovanovich, Inc., New York, 1956.

2 George Gamow, *Thirty Years that Shook Physics: The Story of Quantum Theory*, Anchor Books, Garden City, New York, 1966, p. 61.

3 Many of the details of the early days of the Soviet nuclear programme are taken from Zhores A. Medvedev's *Soviet Science*, Oxford University Press, Oxford, 1979. Another valuable source is Jungk, cited above.

4 A concise history of the development of the nuclear power industry in the Soviet Union by a leading Soviet nuclear energy official is Boris A. Semenov's 'Nuclear power in the Soviet Union,' in the *International Atomic Energy Agency Bulletin*, Vol. 25, No. 2, pp. 47–59. The article was written by Semenov while he was serving as Deputy Director of the IAEA. Semenov is now deputy chairman of the Soviet State Committee on the Utilisation of Atomic Energy.

5 The source for much of the history of the attempt by the American physicists to internationalise atomic energy is Jungk's excellent *Brighter than a Thousand Suns*, cited above.

6 A sketch of the development of international controls on nuclear energy may be found in 'Nuclear Non-Proliferation: Failures and Prospects,' by Ryukichi Imai and Robert Press, in *World Nuclear Energy: Toward a Bargain of Confidence*, Ian Smart, ed. John Hopkins University Press, Baltimore, 1982.

7 Two valuable sources for details of unusual Soviet nuclear energy activities are Semenov's article and an unpublished report, *Nuclear Power in the Soviet Bloc*, by W. P. Geddes. Geddes wrote the report in 1984 as a staff member of the Uranium Institute, a London-based trade association.

8 *Nuclear Power Reactors in the World*, International Atomic Energy Agency, Vienna, April 1986 ed., p. 21.

9 The technical description of the RBMK reactor is taken from Valeri Tolstykh, Document 6621n, *Chernobyl-4: General Plant Description*, International Atomic Energy Agency, Vienna, June 1986.

10 Semenov, op. cit., p. 51.

11 Ibid., p. 48.

12 Thomas J. Connolly, Ulf Hansen, Wolfgang Jaek and Karl-Heinz Beckurts, 'World Nuclear Energy Paths,' in Smart, ed., op. cit., p. 267.

13 Connolly and others, pp. 268–269.

14 Cited in *Uranium: Resources, Production and Demand*, OECD Nuclear Energy Agency and IAEA, Paris, 1986, p. 31.

15 Much of the material in this section comes from a privately prepared paper on Soviet uranium supplies which the author has shared with the proviso that he should not be cited by name.

16 'Afghan rebels say Soviets mine uranium in Afghanistan and ship it back home,' *Nuclear Fuel*, January 16th, 1984, p. 5.

17 Gerald Foley with Charlotte Nassim, *The Energy Question*, second ed., Penguin, Harmondsworth, 1981, p. 164.

18 Semenov, op. cit., p. 48.

19 Imai and Press, op. cit., 'Nuclear Non-Proliferation: Failures and Prospects,' p. 96.

20 Foley and Nassim, op. cit., p. 164.

21 For data on construction, grid connection and other details of reactor operations, see International Atomic Energy Agency, *Nuclear Power Reactors in the World*, April 1986 ed., IAEA, Vienna.

22 Semenov, op. cit., p. 52.8

23 Foley and Nassim, op. cit., p. 165.

24 *Nuclear Power Reactors*, IAEA, p. 51.

25 Most of the details of Soviet press reporting in this section are taken from a Radio Liberty Research paper by Allan Kroncher, entitled 'Soviet Nuclear Power Station Construction Poses Constant Hazards,' RL 194/86, Munich, May 15th, 1986.

26 Much of the information in this section is based on Allan Kroncher, 'What Has Been Happening At Atommash?' Radio Liberty Research Report 281/83, Munich, July 25th, 1983. Subsequent developments have been covered in a variety of western press reports.

27 The Kyshtym accident was originally revealed by Zhores Medvedev in 1976, when he wrote about it in the British journal *New Scientist*. He subsequently added details to his account in two books, *Soviet Science* and *Nuclear Accident in the Urals*. A summary of both the accident and the reaction to it is contained in Rosalie Bertell's *No Immediate Danger:*

Prognosis for a Radioactive Earth, The Women's Press, London, 1985, pp. 175–185.

28 Medvedev, op. cit., p. 94.

5 Preparations for Meltdown

1 USSR State Committee on the Utilisation of Atomic Energy, *The Accident at the Chernobyl Nuclear Power Plant and its Consequences*, Part I, August 1986, p. 2.

2 Material on the Kursk accident comes from USSR State Committee, op. cit., Annex 2, pp. 180–181.

3 IAEA International Nuclear Safety Advisory Group (INSAG), *Summary Report on the Post-Accident Review Meeting on the Chernobyl Accident*, Vienna, September 24th, 1986, p. 101.

4 Telephone interview with Per Persson, a staff member of the safety board of Swedish Utilities, who conducted an analysis of the RBMK reactor for Swedish nuclear safety authorities, September 1986.

5 USSR State Committee, op. cit., Annex 2, p. 131.

6 Many technical details of RBMK plants are taken from a paper by IAEA staff member Valeri Tolstykh, *Chernobyl 4: General Plant Description*, IAEA Document 6621n, IAEA, Vienna, June 1986.

7 The description of the sequence of events leading up to the accident is taken from the official Soviet report cited above with additional detail from the IAEA International Nuclear Safety Advisory Group's summary report, also cited above.

8 USSR State Committee, op. cit., Part I, p. 15.

9 Private conversation with a source who asked not to be identified.

10 The description of the RBMK is taken from USSR State Committee, op. cit.

11 Semenov, op. cit., p. 53.

12 The pressure figures are from IAEA/INSAG, op. cit., p. 127.

13 IAEA/INSAG, op. cit., p. 21.

14 Private conversation with a source who asked not to be identified.

6 The Inferno

1 USSR State Committee on the Utilisation of Atomic Energy, *The Accident At the Chernobyl Nuclear Power Plant and its Consequences*, Part I, August 1986, pp. 17 and 21.

2 USSR State Committee, op. cit., Annex 2, p. 180.

3 Material in this section is based on the official Soviet report of the accident, the IAEA/INSAG analysis of the accident and private conversations with reactor safety specialists.

4 Evidence for this comes from the INSAG report which mentions in passing that certain techniques were *not* used in fighting fires in the control room. Evidence that the control room was irradiated emerged from the explanation Soviet officials have offered for not making control room records available – that the computer tapes and print-outs were heavily irradiated.

5 See the play *Sarcophagus*, by Vladimir Gubarev. Gubarev's play was performed in Moscow and other cities. The fact that it was performed and that the text was published indicate that information in it is not in conflict with the picture the Soviet Union's leaders wish to present of the disaster.

6 Much of this material comes from the first official account of the disaster which was published in May 6th, 1986, edition of *Pravda* and distributed in summary version by the official *Tass* News Agency. Additional details come from a report on the heroism of the firemen carried by the government newspaper *Izvestia* on September 25th and a Soviet television broadcast of the same date.

7 Soviet television report of June 6th, 1986.

8 Details on the use of water are found in IAEA/INSAG, op. cit., pp. 41 and 64–65. There is a brief mention of the subject in USSR State Committee, op. cit., p. 27, although the Soviet report does not mention the danger of flooding the Nos. 1 and 2 units.

9 Interview, Vienna, September, 1986.

10 IAEA/INSAG, op. cit., p. 62.

11 Private comments from a source who requested that he not be identified.

12 USSR State Committee, op. cit., Annex 2, p. 66.

13 IAEA/INSAG, op. cit., p. 78.

14 IAEA/INSAG, op. cit., p. 76.

15 *Sotsialisticheskaya Industriya*, May 16th, 1986, cited by

Theodore Shabad, 'Geographical Aspects of the Chernobyl Nuclear Accident,' *Soviet Geography*, September 1986, p. 509.

16 *Pravda*, June 2nd, 1986, cited in Shabad, p. 510.
17 *Pravda*, June 15th, 1986, cited in Shabad, p. 516.
18 IAEA/INSAG, op. cit., p. 54.
19 *Gudok*, May 16th, 1986, *Izvestia*, May 17th, 1986 and *Stroitel'naya Gazeta*, May 18th, 1986, cited in Shabad, p. 517.
20 *Pravda Ukrainy*, June 26th, cited in Shabad.
21 IAEA/INSAG, op. cit., p. 70.

7 The Dragon's Tail

1 Gofman's remark was widely quoted in wire service reports.
2 Quoted in Robert Jungk, *Brighter than a Thousand Suns: A Personal History of the Atomic Scientists*, Harcourt Brace Jovanovich Inc., New York, 1956, pp. 193–196.
3 See Sir Alan Cottrell, *How Safe is Nuclear Energy?*, Heinemann Educational Books, London and Exeter, 1981, pp. 6–36, for a discussion of radiation and its consequences.
4 See Rosalie Bertell, *No Immediate Danger: Prognosis for a Radioactive Earth*, The Women's Press, London, 1985, pp. 15–63.
5 See Cottrell, op. cit., for examination of the link between radiation and cancer.
6 The story of what happened at Moscow Hospital No. 6 was compiled from Western and Soviet accounts.
7 Dr Robert Gale's estimate. See 'The Victims of Chernobyl,' *Life* Magazine, August 1986, p. 24.
8 Richard Champlin, 'With Chernobyl's Victims,' *Washington Post*, July 13th, 1986.
9 IAEA International Safety Advisory Group Report, IAEA, September 24th, 1986, p. 92.
10 Guskova made her remarks about the bone marrow operations to *Boston Globe* medical writer Larry Tye in an interview at the Chernobyl Post-Accident Review Meeting in Vienna, August 28th, 1986.
11 World Health Organisation, *Chernobyl Reactor Accident: Report of a Consultation*, WHO Regional Office for Europe, Copenhagen, May 6th 1986, p. 31.
12 WHO, op. cit., pp. 6–7.

13 Zbigniew Jaworowski, 'Poland: The First Four Weeks,' *IAEA Bulletin*, Vol. 28, No. 3, Vienna, Autumn 1986, p. 33.

14 IAEA/INSAG Report, op. cit., p. 85.

15 USSR State Committee on the Utilisation of Atomic Energy, *The Accident at the Chernobyl Power Plant and its Consequences*, August 1986, Annex 7, p. 44.

16 USSR State Committee, op. cit., Annex 7, p. 53.

17 See John W. Gofman, *Radiation and Human Health*, Pantheon Books, New York, 1983, foreword.

8 Heroes Against Our Will

1 *Sovetskaya Rossiya*, May 14th, 1986.

2 This chapter was compiled from Soviet and Western press reports. The authors also drew on an excellent analysis of the aftermath of the Chernobyl disaster, 'Geographic Aspects of the Chernobyl Nuclear Accident', by Theodore Shabad, in *Soviet Geography*, No. 7, September 1986. V. H. Winston and Sons, Inc., pp. 504–528. The authors are indebted to both Dr Shabad and Andrew R. Bond for furnishing an advance copy of the article.

3 Revenko's comment was published in *Sovetskaya Rossiya*, on May 7th, 1986, and cited in a *Reuter* dispatch from Moscow on the same day.

4 The authors are entirely indebted for the account of the Estonian conscripts to Toomas Ilves of *Radio Free Europe* Research, Munich. See a number of research papers on the subject, August/September 1986. They include 'Soviet Estonian Paper Admits that Older and Unhealthy Men also Forced to Clean up at Chernobyl,' August 21st; 'Camp Life Among Estonians Cleaning up at Chernobyl,' August 22nd; 'Estonian Daily's Final Instalment on Clean-up Crews at Chernobyl,' August 28th; 'Estonians Help at Chernobyl,' September 10th; 'More on Estonians at Chernobyl: Soviets Respond to the Western Media; Estonian Reported Dead,' September 29th.

5 See Ilves, 'Estonians Help at Chernobyl,' op. cit.

6 See Ilves, 'More on Estonians at Chernobyl,' op. cit.

7 *Sovetskaya Rossiya*, May 14th, 1986.

8 'Ukraine May Have Contaminated Soil for Decades,' *New Scientist*, London, May 15th, 1986.

9 IAEA/INSAG Report, Vienna, September 24th, 1986, p. 88.

9 No-One Thought It Could Happen

1 Avsall was quoted in a *Reuter* report from Copenhagen, September 17th, 1986.
2 The authors used a report by Larry Tye, 'The Lessons of Chernobyl,' *The Boston Globe*, August 30th, 1986.
3 Quoted by Tye, op. cit.
4 Information Policy and Other Measures, a report for the Rainbow Group of the European Parliament, Brussels, 1986. The authors have depended on this excellent and comprehensive report about the European response to Chernobyl.
5 The report was quoted by Tim Dickson, 'Response of EEC Nations to Soviet N-Disaster Condemned,' in the *Financial Times*, August 1st, 1986.
6 Rainbow Group, op. cit.
7 Zamberletti was quoted by E. J. Dionne, *The New York Times*, from Rome on May 10th, 1986.
8 The Swedish official, Jack Valentin, was quoted by Larry Tye, 'The Lessons of Chernobyl,' op. cit.
9 Press Association, parliamentary report, May 8th, 1986.
10 Rainbow Group, op. cit.
11 See Robert Gillette, 'Poland withheld full details of Chernobyl radiation levels,' *Los Angeles Times*, May 31st, 1986.
12 Gillette, op. cit.
13 Quoted by Gillette, 'Chernobyl still casts its shadow on Eastern Europe', *Los Angeles Times*, June 15th, 1986.
14 Pierre Lellouche, *Newsweek*, June 9th, 1986.
15 For an excellent analysis of the emergence of the environmental movement in the Soviet Union see Thane Gustafson, 'Today's Typical Soviet No Longer Passive Peasant,' *Washington Post*, May 4th, 1986. Gustafson is director of the Soviet Studies Programme, Centre for International and Strategic Studies, Georgetown University.
16 See Boris Komarov, *The Destruction of Nature in the Soviet Union*, M. E. Sharpe, Inc., White Plains, New York, 1980, p. 60.
17 Keith Bush, 'Environmental Problems in the USSR,' in *Problems of Communism*, July–August, 1972, p. 25.
18 Komarov, op. cit.
19 Thane Gustafson, op. cit.
20 Komarov, op. cit., p. 9.

10 Atomic Politics

1 International Atomic Energy Agency, *Statute*, IAEA, Vienna, June 1980, p. 5.
2 IAEA Director General Blix and Deputy Director General Konstantinov both declined to be interviewed for this book. Nuclear Safety Director Morris Rosen did grant a request for an interview. Except where otherwise noted all material in this chapter comes from interviews and other materials gathered by the authors personally.
3 According to Western journalists in Warsaw, an official telephone call was made to at least one big Warsaw hospital to inquire about the level of iodine stocks – essential for protection against radioactive iodine – a day before the public announcement of the danger of radiation.
4 IAEA Board of Governors document with restricted circulation.
5 For more detail on IAEA safety programmes, see *IAEA activities in nuclear safety*, IAEA Division of Public Information, Vienna, August 1986.
6 IAEA Press Release PR 87/4, 27 January 1987, *Nuclear Power Reactors in the World*, April 1986 edition, and *Nuclear Research Reactors in the World* (May 1986 edition), IAEA, Vienna.
7 *IAEA activities in nuclear safety*, op. cit., p. 11.
8 For a discussion of conflict of interest, see K. S. Shrader-Frechette, *Nuclear Power and Public Policy: the Social and Ethical Problems of Fission Technology*, D. Reidel Publishing Company, Dordrecht, Holland, 1980.
9 Quotations from Jankowitsch's speech and the other speeches cited in this section come from official texts distributed by the national delegations at the IAEA conference on nuclear safety held in Vienna 24th–26th September, 1986.

11 Counting the Cost

1 IAEA/INSAG Report, September 1986, Vienna., p. 111.
2 *Izvestia*, October 2nd, 1986, reported by *Tass* in English, October 2nd.
3 Judith Thornton, *Soviet Electric Power after Chernobyl: Economic Consequences and Options*, Kennan Institute for

Advanced Russian Studies, The Wilson Center, Washington, 1986, p. 16.

4 Estimate given in private conversation.

5 The Protsenko interview appeared in *Nedelya*, the weekly supplement to the party newspaper *Pravda*, cited by Christopher Walker, *The Times*, London, October 20th, 1986.

6 We are indebted to Albina Tretyakova Birman for this observation, made in private conversation.

7 Soviet television report of speech, 17.00 GMT, September 18th, 1986, cited in British Broadcasting Corporation, *Summary of World Broadcasts*, as *USSR: SWB 22nd Sep. 86 Soviet leader Gorbachev's visit to Krasnodar Kray: address to Kray party activists*. All subsequent quotation from the speech is from the same source.

8 Leonard Silk, 'Arms Stalemate in Iceland: Bad News for Soviet Growth,' *International Herald Tribune*, Paris, October 18th–19th, 1986 p. 17.

9 Personal conversation, July, 1986.

10 All the Burlatsky quotations are from Hamman's transcription of the interview. The other journalists were Fernando Mezzetti, Moscow correspondent of the Italian newspaper *Il Giornale*, and Patrick Cockburn, Moscow correspondent of the *Financial Times*.

INDEX